A lyrical book with a strong poetic element, rich in symbolism ... The story is a gripping one. – *Cape Argus*

Good writing abounds ... a work which compels the reader, literally and figuratively, to carry on. – *Sunday Times*

One of the gems of the book is its abiding respect and awe of the natural assets found in landscape ... Avoid skipping ahead to see whether the group makes it to the top. The suspense is worth it. – *Mail & Guardian*

An inspiring journey of the soul ... This is a book to read in a way you might climb a mountain – slowly ... don't miss the view. – *Cape Times*

The Ziziphus mucronata *is a thorn tree which can be found throughout the entire continent of Africa, extending its boundaries into the Middle Eastern countries of Israel, Lebanon and possibly Turkey. On its branches, it has two rows of thorns, one pointing upwards and out, while the other row hooks back in an opposite direction. It is believed by the traditional Nguni people of southern Africa that these thorns remind us of something about ourselves … they say the ones that point upward and forward tell us that we should always look ahead to the future, while the ones that hook backwards say that we must* never forget where we have come from. *For these people, it is not only the tree of the ancestors, it is the tree of life.*

THORNS TO KILIMANJARO

IAN McCALLUM

DAVID PHILIP PUBLISHERS
Cape Town

First published in 2000 in Southern Africa by David Philip Publishers (Pty) Ltd,
208 Werdmuller Centre, Newry Street, Claremont, 7708, South Africa

First Edition 2000
Second Impression 2001

ISBN 0-86486-359-4

Cover photo by D. Rogers of *Getaway* magazine, Photo Access
Cover design by Abdul Amien

Printed and bound by the Rustica Press, Old Mill Road Ndabeni, Cape Town
D8816

ACKNOWLEDGEMENTS

I wish to thank Janene and Phil Barnard for allowing me to hibernate in their study at a critical time in the writing of this book. To Kobus Geldenhuys who originally edited this manuscript, to my present editor David Philip, and to Sharon, thank you for believing in it. I would like to acknowledge the writer James Hillman, who described best, for me, the meaning of *soul*; and Mark Savage for his comments quoted from *The Walker's Guide and Map to Kilimanjaro*.

This book is dedicated to my wife Sharon.

*It is also my way of saying thank you to my parents and
to my children, Alison, Michelle and Murray …*

1

I HOPE YOU find what you're looking for ...

★　　　★　　　★

'So, this is where we are ...' I whispered.

Exhausted, I stood on the peak of the highest free-standing mountain in the world ... Kilimanjaro. A bitter wind swept up off the snow that sloped upwards toward the summit. It felt its way into my bones as if it had fingers, causing me to pull my neck even deeper into my shoulders. My entire body shivered uncontrollably. Here, on the windswept summit of Africa, I had come to bury my father.

★　　　★　　　★

His name was James Malcolm and he loved that mountain. When I was a boy, he spoke often of a legendary story about a garden situated somewhere in the heart of Africa. It was not far from Ethiopia, he said. In the middle of that ancient garden was a huge mountain. It was called by those who knew it the Mountain of Greatness, and by others the mythological Mount Olympus. It also had another name ... *Ki-li-man-ja-ro*, he said, stretching out the syllables ... *The journey that has no ending.*

'And do you know who told me that?' he asked.

'Who?' I responded, wide-eyed.

'William Phiri.'

'Our William?' I asked, looking toward the kitchen in our home, to see if he was there.

'That's right. He knows all about that mountain. He has never been there, but he says he heard many stories about it when he was a child.'

I remembered William Phiri as a kind of mentor. He was also our domestic cook. He never knew his exact age, but he must have been in his forties when he came to work for my parents, staying on our property in Zambia until his death, when he was in his sixties. He came from the fishing village of Kasanga on the southernmost shores of Lake Tanganyika. From his home, he could look across the lake into Zambia and Malawi. His parents came from Malawi. They had Nguni blood. His family were poor and William was compelled to journey to the copper mines to seek work. Each year, until he died, he visited the village of his birth, bringing gifts of clothing and money. He did not forget where he had come from.

He lived on our smallholding in a red-brick building, called a *khaya*. It was tucked away among the mopane trees about a hundred metres or so behind our homestead, but what I remembered most about it was that the path between the kitchen of our home and his *khaya* was a winding one.

On the subject of James Malcolm and Kilimanjaro, it was easy to imagine myself on its summit, as he spoke.

'From the top,' he would say, 'there was a time when you could look out beyond the forests and the grasslands to the great inland seas of Africa, an apron of curving water around the mountain.

'One day, a very long time ago,' he once said, lowering his voice as though he was telling me a secret, 'there was an upheaval in Africa. Something in the very heart of the ancient continent was brewing and then, like an angry abscess, the land rose up so that the great inland waters tipped away from themselves, leaving in their place dry land and a scar of rupture that still exists today. It was a long scar, like that of a caesarean section,' he added.

My father was a surgeon at the mine hospital where I was born and although I may have heard of him speaking about this kind of operation before, I asked him to explain. He put a finger to his lips, thinking about how he was going to answer me, and then, in a way that I became the very scalpel itself, slicing its way through maternal flesh, he described to me what a caesarean section was and how children are sometimes born this way.

I asked him if I had been born by this kind of delivery. I will never forget his response.

'Nooo …' he said thoughtfully, 'but you do carry the same scar as the one in that ancient valley that I am telling you about. So do I,' he assured me. 'It's the scar of our great-grandfathers and grandmothers. All children have that scar.'

'Where is the scar?' I asked, in amazement. I knew I had no such scar. Or had I?

He took me to a mirror and asked me to take off my shirt. We both stood for a while, looking into our reflections. I could see how skinny I was and how my father's hands easily covered my bony shoulders. I loved his hands. They were gentle, yet masculine. 'There!' he said, tracing his finger down my nose into the groove above my upper lip, across my mouth and along the cleft of my chin, down my neck and into the notch above my breast bone. From there he followed a thin, arrow-like line to my belly button, circled it a couple of times and proceeded downwards, lifting his finger when he came to the top edge of my trousers.

He said the 'scar' was also known as the *linea alba*, the white line, and that all people have it.

'Do you know that the scar of that ancient earthquake is still there today? It's called the Great Rift Valley. They say it's the likely birthplace of the first human beings on this little planet,' he added.

He put his finger onto my navel again and said, 'Do you see this place? It is the deepest point in the rift, that place where you separated from your mother. It's your and my contract as a mammal, the signatures of those who have successfully separated from their mothers.'

He was silent for a while, deep in thought and then he added, 'Imagine that … water falling away from itself, leaving the land to dry out and to heal in its own way. Imagine you and me, Hamish, born out of amniotic waters like that, into another world … a world of air. One thing *becoming* something else,' he mused.

'And there,' he said, pointing again into the mirror, 'the longitudinal scar.'

'I'm going to go there one day,' he added. 'I am going to trace out that *journey that has no ending* and I'm going to take William Phiri with me.'

'These worlds I tell you of are not unreal,' he used to say. 'Born out of the capacity to imagine, they are just different kinds and different stages of reality.'

My father often spoke poetically like this, catapulting me into strange and wonderful worlds, capturing me with his vivid imagination and his deep sense of history.

Although I didn't always understand what he was saying, I liked what he said. Perhaps, I liked the *way* he said it. Poetry has a way of getting to the heart of things.

As I look back, there were times when I thought he was a god. Born in the west of Scotland, he grew up on the Celtic coastline of the Mull of Kintyre. Although he loved his homeland and his ancestral roots, he found it impossible to live there, not because of the sometimes cold and inclement weather, or the rolling mists that so often blanketed what he called his beloved highlands, but because of an unforgettable experience when he was a surgical registrar at the Royal Infirmary in Edinburgh. During a short vacation to the south of Spain, he ended up in Gibraltar, and looking across the great straits toward the south, he saw the coast of Morocco and, beyond that, the rising highlands of north Africa.

As if urged on by an unknown hand, he took the ferry to Tangier, and as he set foot on African soil for the first time in his life something seemed to leap up through his feet, a kind of warmth that raced up into his solar plexus, settling somewhere in his belly and staying there. Turning to a woman whom he did not know, but who had been on board the ferry, he whispered, 'I know this place. I have come home.'

'It was just one of those things. It was like a calling,' my mother once told me. She was the woman on the ferry.

I inherited a few things, besides perhaps a few physical traits, from my father, one of which unsettled my mother. It was my love of mountains. I am told that it was the same for him, but if I was asked what it was that drew me to mountains, I would say that it was the sensing of a sometimes unbelievable indifference that mountains have for human beings. I like that. But, there is something else about them that haunts me. It is a silence that can almost be measured. It is a silence that demands that one should ask its permission to be there.

★   ★   ★

I also inherited his fascination for medicine. He loved his work and I loved to listen to him speaking about it. I resonated with his stories of what it was that gave people a sense of meaning in their lives. What made medicine fascinating, he said, was when you began to link it to mythology. He believed that many medicines have something 'special', a peculiar ingredient which transcends its chemical formula. They carry a *story*, an ingredient of *meaning*, he said, which cannot be measured, and without which the medicine would probably not be as effective. He believed that healing and mending were not the same thing. I didn't know what he meant then, but I would come to know. *Meaning* was central to *healing*, he once said.

He was more than a medical doctor, I later realised. He was a medicine man.

2

A LONG WAY from home, I was in my sixth and final year at boarding-school in Cape Town when the postcard arrived from the 'bush', which is what I called home. It is still like that today. Home for me will always be the 'bush'. That, I have learned, is where my *medicine* is.

It was lunchtime on a hot February afternoon and the post was being handed out in the boarding-house dining-room. 'This one comes from a long way,' said the post monitor. He handed me the card. I looked at the black-and-white picture of the snow-capped dome of a mountain and then turned it around and saw the Tanganyika postage stamp on it. My father's handwriting was also unmistakable: 'Greetings from the highest and deepest places in Africa – Kilimanjaro and Olduvai Gorge. It is not very far from where you are. It is *inside* you. I will be writing soon. As aye, Dad and William Phiri.'

'They did it!' I whispered excitedly … the journey that has no ending.

That night I lay awake for a long time. I couldn't help wondering what had suddenly made him do it *then*.

★   ★   ★

When he arrived back in Nkana from Tanganyika my father wrote me a long letter about their climb. I still have that letter today.

There were no other climbers on the mountain then, just the two of them, their guide and a couple of porters. This was the clothing that they took with them: leather mining boots, long-john underwear, jerseys and woollen balaclava head-warmers. Old Mr 'Polly', the engineer from the Training Centre at Nkana mine, had organised for steel studs to be fitted into the soles of their boots, in case they had to walk through ice, which they did.

When it was all over, he was glad to be home again. The mountain had been an amazing adventure which had made him think a little differently about life. There were many times when he had wondered what the hell he was doing there and would he not have been better off had he stayed at home. Only idiots put themselves through such physical stress, he wrote. The altitude got to him, often making him feel that his head was in an iron vice.

'I kept telling William to go on because the only thing I wanted to do was to sleep. I would never have made it without him. He repeatedly urged me on with these words, *pol-e, pol-e*, Swahili for slowly, slowly. I chanted these words all the way to the top.'

He enclosed two photographs taken at the summit. One of them he took himself. He said he didn't have the energy to take more. It was taken while he was lying on his back on Kibo Peak. All you could see in the photograph were his boots against a blurred background of sky and clouds. He said he was so tired when he took the picture, he could only do it while he was lying down. He was actually hoping to get a shot of Mount Meru in the distance, but he didn't have the energy to focus the camera properly! The other photograph was of him holding a rectangular stainless-steel container. William took this one. On the back of the print he wrote, 'Inside this canister is a wee bible that your granddad gave me when I left Scotland as a young man. As you know, he too loved the mountains and I told him that I would take it to the top of Africa with me one day. I left it on Kibo Peak in memory of him. It was also a way of saying thank you to Kilimanjaro for allowing me to be there. Incidentally, if you squint your eyes you can see Scotland from up here!'

He signed off in dialect, I could hear his voice:

'*We miss ye 'roon the hoos.*' (We miss you around the house.) With love from me and your mother, As aye, Mum and me – Dad.'

There was a postscript on a separate page. It was a story about a brooding Italian man who was being held as a prisoner of war near Dar es Salaam during the 1940s. His name was not forgotten, it was unknown. He would not tell his name. What is remembered, however, was his escape. It was a futile exercise, they said. Crazy! To journey as a fugitive through Kenya, Ethiopia and the deserts of the north was impossible. To weave his way to the ports on the Indian Ocean meant certain recapture. All roads to the sea were guarded.

For three weeks there was no sound or sight of the Italian. Then, as suddenly and as unexpectedly as his escape, he returned to the camp looking sunburnt and radiant. 'I did it!' was all he said.

★   ★   ★

I have learned a thing or two about high-altitude mountains and the amount of preparation that is necessary to challenge them. It amazes me even now that James Malcolm and William Phiri actually made it to the top. There was no fancy climbing gear in those days, no lightweight gortex boots or polypropylene thermal underwear, nothing like that.

★   ★   ★

Four months after receiving that postcard, my parents, in a surprise visit, came to see me at boarding-school. When I saw them I was both thrilled and puzzled. What were they doing here, I wondered? What was happening? We hugged and kissed each other warmly and then I looked at my father. His eyes had a glassy look. It was a look of urgency. I could tell by my mother's expression that she was concerned. 'Dad has not been feeling well for the past month,' she said. 'There've been night sweats, he's been losing weight and the doctors back home suspected that he had malaria. They couldn't find any parasites in his blood, but they treated him for it all the same. It didn't help. They said he needed some special tests, so the physician back home suggested that he take a trip to Johannesburg to have a few tests done.'

By the time the family had arrived in Cape Town, the tests had already been done.

'They said the results would take a few days, so we decided on a wee holiday,' said my father, his west-of-Scotland accent coming across more pronounced than I had heard it for a long time. He said he was going to call in on the doctors in Johannesburg for the results on the way home.

He looked different. He was thinner and there was a quietness about him. Picking up on my concern, he smiled wryly and said, 'I'm not so bad. I'm sure I'll be all right.' He changed the subject and asked me if I remembered him telling me that he always wanted to climb Kilimanjaro.

I nodded, wondering what he was getting at. 'Well, it turned out to be the other way round,' he said. 'That mountain climbed *me*. I'm still recovering.'

My mother shook her head in silence. I could see the frustration in the frowns on her forehead, or was it despair? Looking at my father, she said, 'You know as well as I do that you were off-colour when you made up your mind to go. You were tired. There was far too much night work.' She turned to me. 'I couldn't stop him,' she said. 'He believed the mountain would fix him. He said it would be his *medicine*.'

'And it was,' my father replied with a hint of a grin.

My stomach buzzed with a tangible feeling of uncertainty and I caught myself clenching my jaw. I suggested we take a stroll in the school grounds. I wanted to get away from the prying eyes of the boarders, who were watching the interaction between my parents and me. We sat down together on a bench beneath a leaf-less oak-tree, naked in its winter phase. There were small, pregnant swellings on the branches, a promise of the new leaves that would give the tree its spring cloak.

'You don't find trees like this one in central Africa,' said my father, studying the extensive branches and the thick trunk of the old Cape exotic.

'What do you mean, Dad? The mountain climbed *you*?' I asked, anxious to get onto the same wavelength as him.

'On those slopes, I was struck by what it means to live in a world of paradoxical *time* ... to live both in a world of clockwork and in a world of time. I know life is short, but up there I was reminded that I had all the time in the world. It was as though the world slowed down for me. It's very difficult to explain, but in a strange way, I felt old, yet I was brand-new. I could have been looking at the world the way that the *first* people must have seen it ... like the allegorical Adam of Genesis. I felt a sense of participation with the trees, the birds and the animals. I belonged. Someone once called this phenomenon *participation mystique*, a lovely expression,' he said, referring to the almost mystical way in which the traditional hunter-gatherers lived interdependently with the environment. 'For me, there was nothing mystical about it,' he stated, dropping his eyes. 'It was a healing experience. It was real.'

It was the first time that he had ever done that: not looking at me when he spoke to me, as if he was hiding something.

The gnawing wave of uncertainty filled my belly again. I was afraid.

I knew he was going to die.

*   *   *

How could a man speak of a healing experience when he was dying? I would later remember what he had said about healing and mending ... *healing* and *mending* were not necessarily the same thing. I would also learn that there is no healing without a profound sense of connection with life ... that, like water and blood, life takes a winding path ... it seems to know where it is going.

*   *   *

My mother phoned me from Johannesburg. The news wasn't good. The cancer had already taken hold in his body. The doctors said if only he had come to see them sooner … *before* he had gone to the mountain, they may have been able to cure him. I knew they were not talking about healing.

★   ★   ★

It took William Phiri and my father four and a half days and four nights to climb Kilimanjaro, 'to come home' as he put it. It took the same time to travel by train from Cape Town to Nkana. I was going home to say goodbye.

Death was close and my father knew it. Coming out of the bathroom one morning, he said, 'I looked into the mirror just now and beheld a disappearing man!' He gave a whimsical smile, one that used to make me giggle. Right then I wanted to weep.

Beethoven's *Violinromanz* played softly in the background. Seated in our lounge, my mother was writing Christmas cards. I pretended to be reading but I was looking over the top of my book at my father who was seated nearby. Every now and then he would catch my eye, and I would look away. He knew I was watching him leaving Africa.

Suddenly, our dog growled. 'Hush!' admonished my mother, but the dog did not listen to her. He began to bark and the ridge on his back bristled. Then came the loud, impatient knock at the front door.

I leapt up and on opening the door confronted a tall, muscular man with a large grin on his face.

'Is your pa here?' the man asked.

'Dad, it's someone to see you.'

'Well, invite him in.'

James Malcolm pulled his thin frame up out of his chair and took a few breaths before approaching the visitor who was now standing in the hallway. He noticed the little stainless-steel tin that the man was carrying in his right hand and immediately recognised it as the container he had taken to Kilimanjaro.

'I thought you people might have wanted this back again,' said the stranger, a big man, with a short back-and-sides haircut. He said he was on his way back to a nearby mine town where he lived and worked. The man's speech and his accent told us that he came from South Africa, where English was probably not his home language. He said he was in a bit of a hurry and wasted no time telling us that he had won a bet for getting to the top of Kilimanjaro. This was his 'proof', he said, holding up the container.

My father was having difficulty breathing. The man was jabbering on about how some of the party didn't make it to the top and how they had gone about it all wrong and that the 'kaffirs' in Tanganyika were 'screwing up the country'.

'Kilimanjaro was a piece of cake. How did you find it?' he asked.

'I found it north-west of the village of Moshi,' said my father, in a matter-of-fact response.

The man gave my father a puzzled look and then said that he had to go. 'There are people waiting for me,' he smiled.

Turning to go, the man, who never gave his name, said, 'Oh yes, if anyone should phone and ask about me, tell them that I wasn't lying … that I brought back your tin for you.'

'I wish you had just left it where it belonged,' my father responded. 'Good night,' he added, closing the door behind him with a soft click.

He stood with his back to us for a while and then said, 'He didn't need proof of what he had done. It was in his eyes.'

He then slowly opened the silvery container and looked inside. The small bible was still there. It looked weather-beaten. Some of its pages had come loose and lay stacked in the canister, separated from the jacket of the book. He replaced the pages and then very quietly announced, 'The book of Genesis is missing. It has probably scattered itself on that wind-swept mountain.'

'Strange …' he said, pausing long before speaking again, 'my own father said that Genesis was the most significant book of them all … when you understood it.'

★ ★ ★

Two days later, James Malcolm died at his home in Nkana. William Phiri was with us at his bedside.

At his request the minister read these words for him at his funeral:

And the earth was without form and void; and darkness was upon the face of the deep. And the spirit of God moved upon the face of the waters.

And God said, Let there be light: and there was light.

… The earth brought forth grass, the herb yielding seed, and the fruit tree yielding fruit after his kind, whose seed was in itself.

Why did he choose those verses? What was he trying to say? For a moment I began to see the image of something that wanted to be born into the world, something that was looking for a face … and a voice. And then I saw the image of water falling away from itself. Unconsciously, I fingered the midline 'scar' of my body through my shirt. It hurt.

In his eulogy to James Malcolm, my uncle described my father as a man who tried to live his life poetically, embracing in his own way the laws of science with the rhythms of art.

The minister then called upon me to read one of my father's favourite poems, written by Rainer Maria Rilke. I knew it off by heart, but I had it down on paper, just in case. I had never stood in front of a congregation before. Looking out at the sea of faces in front of me, I went cold. I searched for my tongue and then my eyes found the distant face of William Phiri. Raising his eyebrows, he nodded his head to say that it was going to be all right.

> *Sometimes a man stands up during supper*
> *and walks outdoors, and keeps on walking,*
> *because of a church that stands somewhere in the East.*
>
> *And his children say blessings on him as if he were dead.*
>
> *And another man, who remains inside his own house,*
> *stays there, inside the dishes and in the glasses,*
> *so that his children have to go far out into the world*
> *toward that same church, which he forgot.*

My throat ached and like walking through a mist, I found my way to the pew where I sat down heavily next to my mother. She put her hand on my thigh and after a few moments, I gently pushed it away. I did not wish to be held. I wanted to be alone.

And then I became angry ... angry at the doctors, angry with medicine, angry with the mountain. Stuff his mountain, I thought. Stuff his mythology! Stuff his church!

It was an anger that would stay with me for a long time.

3

SPRING ALWAYS ARRIVES late in Cape Town. It is supposed to warm up in September and even though the Cape daffodils and the dazzling wild spring flowers of Namaqualand have come and gone, many Capetonians are sent scurrying for their pullovers as late as November, chilled by approaching cold fronts from the Antarctic. It was a morning such as that when my wife, Jessie, sent me up into the attic to retrieve the oil heater that I had prematurely consigned to its summer resting place. I remembered being amazed at how much dust could accumulate in an attic in such a short period. Unlike the European attics, which are often converted into spare living quarters, attics in southern Africa are usually storage spaces in the rafters of homes. The usual way into them is via a trapdoor in the ceiling of one of the rooms, sometimes requiring a stepladder and a more than average arm-strength to lever oneself into the roof space. This pretty much describes our attic.

I lowered the heater down to my teenage son, who was waiting at the foot of the ladder, grumbling that I had disturbed him from his studies. Before closing the trapdoor, I scanned the attic to make sure that there was nothing else that I had to bring down. At the far end I saw the old trunk I used to have as a schoolboy, the one that went up and down on the old 'Rhodesian' train, from Cape Town to Nkana, twice a year, four and a half days up, four and a half days down … all those years ago. Dented and in need of a coat of paint, it had become the receptacle for old documents and discarded photographs. There must have been a lot of useless information in that old trunk.

I was about to descend the ladder, when I suddenly became aware of an urge to examine the contents of the trunk. I tried to deny it at first. After all, I knew exactly what was in that trunk … or did I? The urge intensified.

I pulled myself up through the trapdoor again, wiped the dust off my hands on the back of my trousers and walked over to the trunk. Over the years, the hinges had rusted and the lid opened with a grating noise that sent a shiver down my back. As expected, it was filled with files and newspaper cuttings. At the top of the heap was a file of rugby reports from my student days. I paged through them with a half-smile on my face. It was like yesterday. Out of the corner of my eye I saw a small moth – a silverfish – taking cover from the light, scampering into the depths of the trunk. I tried to follow it, knowing how destructive they were in their appetite for paper. The little creature disappeared beneath a pile of papers and, as I lifted them, I was distracted by my reflection on the surface of a stainless-steel tin.

I drew a breath and stood still in hesitation, deciding whether or not to pick up the container. My conviction of what was inside that old tin was followed by a wave of doubt. I lifted it out of the trunk and felt its cold, metallic surface on my fingers. Suddenly images of inland seas and caesarean sections came rushing into my head. I heard the loud knocking at the door of my boyhood home in Nkana and I heard the groaning voice of the minister at the funeral service. A momentary wave of anger swept over me, but I ignored it. Instead, I opened up the little tin. Was the lid tight from misuse or was it my hands that were shaking? I saw the loose pages protruding from the edge of the bible and when I opened the jacket I read, for the first time, a message from my grandfather to his son, James Malcolm, written in light upstroke, heavy down stroke, cursive handwriting. It read: *Re-member Genesis, my son, and may the Great Spirit of Africa be with you. Dad.*

I had never seen that message before. It was beautiful. Reading it again, I noticed the hyphenation of the word remember ... *Re-member*. What did he mean? I then noticed that the book of Genesis was missing.

Another wave of anger hit me, catching me by surprise. Where did that come from, I asked myself? 'Cool it!' I said aloud. And then came another.

These waves of anger were not unfamiliar to me – I had often experienced them. I used to put them down to the demanding work at the hospital or to the sometimes short-sighted bureaucratic bungling in the local health services. Sometimes I thought they were due to the frustration of not having enough time to myself. I often felt a need to be away from my children, even if it was for a day or two. Maybe they needed to be away from me.

In spite of my rationalising, something in me knew better. Something else, something unresolved, was keeping the anger alive in me. I didn't want to believe it at first, but as I stood there in that attic, I began to realise that it had something to do with James Malcolm, my father. I then remembered the funeral service, Rilke's poem and my need to be alone. I remembered cursing his mountain and his church. Was it possible that I was harbouring a deep, unexpressed anger towards him? If so, why, for heaven's sake? Then it occurred to me ... *For dying when he did!*

I realised there was so much that I wanted to show him, so much that he didn't know about me – that I had become a doctor, that he had grandchildren and that he didn't know their mother, Jessie Williams. He would have loved her.

'What are you doing up here?' Startled out of my distant thoughts, I turned around to see Jessie's grinning face peering into the attic from the top of the stepladder.

'Your eyes are moist ... are you okay?' she asked. Jessie was never one to beat about the bush.

'Come and have a look at this, sweetheart,' I replied, motioning her toward the old trunk and the little tin container in my hand. I helped her up through the trapdoor.

I then opened the lid of the tin and showed her my father's bible, with the message from my grandfather on the inside cover. 'Look … the book of Genesis is missing. Do you remember me telling you about this before?' Jessie nodded. I then told her about the waves of anger.

'I think I know what it is about,' I said. 'I'm angry with my father, believe it or not.' I was also angry with his god – for taking him when he did. To me, it was not a god of capital letters and in any case, after my father's premature death, I didn't know how anyone could believe in the likelihood of an all-loving deity. I had been angry at that system of religious thought for a long time.

Jessie, who had attended a girls' convent in Grahamstown and who probably had ten times as much religious instruction as I'd had, stood silently at my side for a while. 'Honey … that's the most encouraging thing I have heard from you in a long time.'

'What do you mean?'

'I've been aware of that anger in you. I have seen you sublimating it into your sport and the long hours you spend at the hospital. I had a fair idea where it came from, but I didn't want to push it. Your father was like a hero for you, wasn't he? How do you acknowledge anger for someone like that?'

'It's very difficult being angry at someone for dying,' she continued. 'I know that. And yet, there are times when you have to be … it is a part of the grieving process, you know.' I looked Jessie in the eye, but remained silent.

'The fact that you've possibly acknowledged its source is a major realisation, Hamish. It is all the more significant if you want to learn how to come to terms with it. But it had to come from you,' she said, letting out a deep sigh.

I felt as if there was a huge weight coming off my shoulders and I too let out a deep breath.

'Do you know what I am thinking?' she gently asked, looking me in the eye.

'What?'

'Take the bible back for him. You might find Genesis on the way.'

'To the top of Kilimanjaro?'

I stood there shaking my head in some kind of denial. It was as if I was confronting someone or something in me and telling it, 'No … no … no.' But I could not deny what I was hearing. The 'voice' said, 'Go … go … go.'

Descending the stepladder, I looked down and noticed that one of my shoelaces was undone. Safely on the ground, I retied it and, in doing so, I had an inkling that there were other loose ends in my life.

'What do you mean – I might find Genesis?'

'Well, have you ever really looked at it?' she asked, knowing that any serious study on my part was unlikely, which I subsequently confirmed.

'You mean all the begets and the begats?'

'No …' said Jessie seriously, 'I'm referring to the profound personal significance of the story. Those first few chapters are not simply an allegorical or historical account of our beginnings. When looked at psychologically, they are as relevant today as when Moses first wrote them. Genesis is a work of art, you know … a blue-print for the initiation of the artist in us. It is a fascinating account of the necessary task of learning how to leave our mothers and fathers. You have a love for Nietzsche, don't you? Can you remember what he said about the artist?'

'Remind me,' I answered.

'He said the task of the artist is *god-making* … which as I understand it, is the task of giving God a human face. I'm not saying I'm right but that is what I think those chapters in Genesis are about.' I stood there, trying to digest what she had said.

'Have you seen this?' I asked, pointing to the message from my grandfather.

'What do you make of the hyphen … re-member?'

Jessie thought for a while. 'Do you think he may have been trying to convey the word as a re-membering, a putting together again, rather than not forgetting?'

'I like that,' I said … 'to *re-member*.'

That night I began reading the opening chapters of Genesis.

★ ★ ★

Jessie had been in practice as a clinical psychologist for nearly twelve years, working under her maiden name, Jessica Williams. I remember her once telling me, 'You can only go as far with your client as you have gone with yourself.' That stuck with me for a long time. There was something honest in that.

I knew the metaphor of a mountain was hidden in that statement.

4

FROM A WINDOW seat in front of the left wing of the Air Tanzania Boeing 737, I could see the profile of a mountain rising up out of the ground. I followed it upward and saw that its summit disappeared into thick clouds. I held my breath for a while, wondering if that was it. It must be, I thought.

'Take a look at that, Jessie. I think that could be it.'

'Oh God! Is that Kilimanjaro?' she exclaimed.

It was a little over five hours since we had taken off from Johannesburg International Airport. Jessie had insisted on going with me. Her words still echoed, 'I'd rather go with you to the top of that mountain than hear you telling me what it's like.'

We had flown up from Cape Town the night before, to meet up with my old university friends, Hugh Butler and Brian Cupido.

Hugh and I had often spoken about 'doing' Kilimanjaro some day, but what we didn't know then was that no one 'does' Kilimanjaro. It 'does' you – as my father had told me.

Hugh had arrived that afternoon from Botswana to join us for the climb. A part-owner of a game concession in the Oka-vango Delta, he was a man with an amazing understanding of animal behaviour and was regarded by some of his colleagues as one of the best game trackers in the business. During our varsity days, I played as inside-half, while Hugh and Brian were the centre three-quarters in the same university rugby side. Hugh was quick, agile and a fearless tackler. On the field, his

21

long hair was contained by a headband. He was and looked conspicuously exciting. Sartorially, he was ahead of his time, for in those days in South Africa anyone with long hair was regarded as either a hippie or a communist. He was neither. He was apolitical, bright and hard-working and he cruised through his degree, *cum laude*, majoring in the unlikely combination of Roman and Greek History and Zoology. He loved animals and he loved mythology. In a way, he reminded me of my father.

Brian, on the other hand, was as solid as a rock in his mid-field partnership with Hugh. He was 'Mr Reliable'… nothing fancy, not as athletically gifted as Hugh, but a great tackler.

When I told Hugh of our plans to travel to Tanzania, he simply replied, 'I'm there! What about Brian?'

Brian joked that he had a fear of heights. He told us that he had once climbed the Tower of London 'with oxygen assistance'. He had an infectious sense of humour, but that was not all. He was a determined, self-made man who owned his own engineering company in Johannesburg.

Unlike Hugh and me, Brian had strong political leanings. He saw the world not through the eyes of biological science or mythology, but through the experience of a man whose family had previously been regarded as second-class citizens in South Africa. Brian was a coloured man in an *apartheid* country. In spite of his political frustrations in what can only be regarded as a dark age in my adopted homeland's history, Brian was one of the few men I knew who seemed to be genuinely comfortable with himself. He had dignity. Another way of looking at it was that he refused to be a victim. 'It is *my* choice whether I want to be a victim of those political dinosaurs or not,' he once said. 'And I refuse to be one.'

He knew that the major pillars of ethnic divisions were fear and ignorance. 'Show me a person who says he knows exactly how a black man's or a coloured man's mind works,' he had said, 'and I will show you a man who has been taught how to think like that. I will also show you what that man is afraid of.'

Jessie was leaning across me and I pushed back on my seat to give her a good look through the small oval window of the aircraft. Hugh and Brian were sitting in front of us. A man sitting directly behind me leaned between our seat and said, 'That's it! I would recognise that bitch anywhere!'

I presumed he was referring to the mountain and I turned to meet the voice. It belonged to a well-built man in his forties, with greying, short-cropped hair. He was wearing a khaki shirt that was unbuttoned to his mid-chest. His sleeves were rolled up, revealing powerful forearms, with a fading tattoo on the left one.

I looked at him with raised eyebrows and nodded my head but I didn't say anything.

'Have you climbed Kilimanjaro before?' Jessie inquired, not at all put off by his abrupt manner. Avoiding Jessie's question, he said, 'It's a bit of a boring climb. My old man did it some time ago. He said it rained like hell.'

Sitting there listening to the man's unsolicited opinions left me having to deal with two things. One, that I had taken an instant dislike to him, and two, that there was this strange sense of familiarity … that I either knew the man from somewhere, or that I knew someone like him.

The man continued to advise us. 'They say this is the best time to come here. It's the dry season.'

Feeling increasingly irritable, I wondered who *they* were. *They* say this or *they* say that. Having worked in a government hospital, I soon learned that *they* was an amorphous bureaucratic phenomenon. Trying to find out who *they* were was an impossible task. *They* didn't exist.

'Have you blokes come to climb as well?' he asked.

I nodded my head again and looked away, hoping that he would leave us to savour the view, but he was not taking the hint.

'I suppose you booked your trip through a safari company?' he guessed correctly. 'And which one, if I might be so bold as to ask?' he persisted.

'African Adventures,' answered Jessie. 'They gave us a good deal. We've been very happy with them,' she added. I picked up that she too was becoming irritated.

'Oh, *them,*' he said with authority, 'they're okay, but some of them, some of those others … they really rip you off! It's actually much cheaper organising your own group, especially if you're prepared to lead it yourself, like I'm doing. That's where the money is. These are the people I'm taking with me,' he said, gesturing with his head to a group of passengers across the aisle.

'Good luck to you,' Jessie said, turning away and leaning across me again to look out of the window. The plane banked sharply to the right which seemed to shut the man up for a bit. He eased himself back into his seat and then reached forward for the in-flight magazine in the pouch behind Jessie's seat. I could hear him flicking the pages. Everything about him was loud. I realised that I had let him get to me. I couldn't place him, but the feeling that I knew him from somewhere persisted. Maybe it was his abrasive 'know-all' attitude that put me off him. All I knew was that I didn't like him. I hoped I wouldn't see him again.

★   ★   ★

A big part of Jessie's training in psychotherapy was to identify the phenomenon of *projections*. Negative projections are both primitive and immature defence mechanisms of the ego, attributing or projecting onto others what you don't like or can't accept in yourself. It is an unconscious process. Jessie puts it this way, 'When a person walks into a room – someone you do not know – and you take an instant dislike to him, it's often because he reminds you of something that you don't like in yourself. '

★   ★   ★

Jessie gently squeezed my thigh and whispered into my ear, 'Don't let him get to you.'

The plane banked steeply in its final descent to Kilimanjaro International Airport. I held Jessie's hand and she put her head on my shoulder. I knew what her body language was about. She was there not only to climb the mountain, but to be with me on a peculiar journey. I had come to bury my father in a way that I least expected. I wondered if this was going to be one of those journeys – the ones that have no ending? My mother had suddenly become involved.

A tall, good-looking woman with streaks of grey in her sandy brown hair, my mother lived in a small but comfortable cottage near our home. She must have seen me walking toward her cottage a few weeks ago, because she opened the door before I had a chance to knock. She saw the stainless-steel tin in my hand but did not say anything until she had shown me to the lounge and had closed the door behind me.

'Can you remember how disappointed Dad was when that man came to the house with that container?' she asked, without looking at me.

'So you know what's in here,' I said. She gave me a knowing look. I told her Jessie and I were going to Kilimanjaro and that I wanted to take it back for him.

'Good!' she said in a completely matter-of-fact way. 'He would love that,' referring to my father as though he was alive. 'There is something else that he would like you to do for him … if you don't mind.'

I got up from the easy chair and followed her into her bedroom. On the yellowwood kist beside her bed was a photograph of Jessie and me on our wedding day. There was also a picture of my father and me. We had been fishing together. I must have been about fourteen years old then.

Shifting the photographs and the bedside lamp from the kist, she lifted the lid and gently moving aside some of her winter garments stored there, she removed a wooden box, slightly longer and deeper than the metal container I held in my hand. She closed the kist, straightened the lace cover and replaced the photographs before standing up and facing me. What was inside *that*, I wondered. It was as if I did not want to know.

'Son, these are your father's ashes,' she said, looking into my eyes with a half-smile. 'I knew that you would go there one day, and so did he, but no one was to force it on you, he said. He asked if you could please take something of him with you.'

Mom's eyes were moist as she searched mine for an answer. I stepped forward and held her in my arms.

5

KILIMANJARO INTERNATIONAL AIRPORT, situated almost halfway between the towns of Arusha and Moshi, was specifically designed and built to cater for tourists en route to either the Serengeti Plains or the 'Mountain of Greatness'. The airport had known better days. The large red-and-white-painted radar screen above the control tower was the home to three or four large crows' nests. I wondered when last the radar screen had worked.

An east wind from the Indian Ocean and the Tanzanian lowlands was blowing. I could feel its dryness on my face. It was the warm wind of the dry season − a good time to climb the mountain, we had been told.

Inside the airport terminus the immigration official looked through my passport. He said he wanted the documents that showed that my wife and I had been inoculated against yellow fever and cholera.

Jessie pointed to the customs form that she had filled in and asked me, 'Do I put down three or two where it asks how many family members are with us?'

I frowned. 'Two, of course.' I thought it was an odd question from Jessie.

'What about your father?' she teased, nudging me in the ribs. I suddenly paled.

The customs man poked at my baggage with his finger and asked me what I had brought for him. It suddenly occurred to me that he might decide to search my baggage. I did not know what to say or what he would do if he happened to open up the casket containing the ashes. I told him that the only things that I had brought with me were items that I needed for Kilimanjaro. 'But there is another thing that I have brought,' I said. 'It is the best wishes from my father.'

The customs official looked at me askance.

'Sir,' I addressed him, 'my father came to your beautiful country forty years ago. He climbed your great mountain with his Tanzanian friend, Mr William Phiri, who came from Kasanga in the south.'

The man's eyebrows raised.

'My father is dead now,' I said. 'Where I come from we believe he is with the ancestors, but my mother is alive. When I told her that I was coming to do what my father had done, she said his spirit would be on the mountain … waiting for me.'

The man grinned and indicated with his head that Jessie and I could pass through.

Someone said a bus was going to pick us up at the airport and take us to our hotel in Moshi. Apparently it would not take too long before it arrived and so, with nothing to do, I looked towards the mountain that I had seen from the Boeing. It was to the west of where I was standing and its profile was silhouetted by the sun, which by then was getting low in the sky. Clouds still hid its peak and I began to imagine myself on its slopes. I thought about it for a while and then decided that Kilimanjaro did not look quite as daunting as I had originally expected it to be.

★   ★   ★

I looked ahead of me and saw a large flamboyant tree in full, red-blooded bloom. I knew these trees well. They were among my favourites and even though they originally came from the subcontinent of the Near East, they had made themselves at home in most of central Africa. We had one in our garden in Nkana, where I grew up. It was nearly as big as the one in front of me. The flamboyant tree gives wonderful shade and is quite brilliant when it is in flower. Seeing it in this kind of fullness gave me a feeling of home-coming. Jessie, who also grew up in Zambia and was admiring the tree too, was thinking the same thing.

'I feel as if I've been here before,' she said. Its red flowers in the late afternoon light had become the same colour as the sun which, by then, had only a little way to go before it dropped below the dusty horizon.

Near the tree, in the middle of a circular traffic island, was a flagpole. The wind was flicking the flag ropes against it in a rhythmic, yet monotonous, *kachink … kachink … kachink*. It was an unmistakable metallic sound which in the past one hundred and fifty years had become an integral part of Africa. It was the 'kachinking' echo of days gone by, when much of the continent was under colonial rule. I imagined the British, the Portuguese, the Germans and the Italians hoisting their flags all over Africa.

A frayed, somewhat exhausted-looking Tanzanian flag flapped away lethargically in the warm easterly breeze.

I then saw another tree that I immediately recognised as a *Ziziphus mucronata*. We had one of these on our Zambian property as well. William Phiri first told me about these trees. They were special trees for him … and they became so, for me.

I will never forget the way William described its leaves and its unique thorns to me.

If you look at its leaves, he said, you will see that, among the green ones, there are always some that are yellow and some that are brown. He told me that the green leaves represented youth, the yellow leaves the years of adulthood and the brown ones old age.

Moving closer to the tree, I saw the double row of thorns on its branches, one row pointing robustly forward and out, the other curving gently backwards and in. I remembered what William Phiri had said about that … 'Keep moving, look ahead, say the forward-pointing thorns, while the other ones, the ones that hook, say, *Never forget where you have come from.*'

Another thing of significance for my old mentor was that the *Ziziphus* was closely linked to the ancestors. If someone should die a long way from home, that person's spirit could not rest until it had been brought back to the village. One way of getting it back, was to 'carry' it in a branch of a *Ziziphus* that came from the village.

I thought about the two great trees in Genesis … *the tree of life also in the midst of the garden, and the tree of the knowledge of good and evil.* Did they have thorns, I wondered?

I went up to the tree and greeted it quietly. Maybe it had something to do with my early boyhood, growing up in the bush and the many trees in our garden, but I have always seen trees as people.

I asked permission from the *Ziziphus* to break one of its smaller branches. I told it there was somebody close to me who now lived among the ancestors and whose spirit wished to be brought back to the Great Mountain. I waited for a while and when the feeling was right, I broke off a branch and placed it in the side pocket of my rucksack, alongside the container that carried my father's ashes.

Hugh strolled up toward me. 'Do you know what this tree is called?' he asked.

I nodded my head, 'Yes, I do … it is from the old Arabic word *zizouf* which means lotus. The Nguni people call it the tree of life.' I then told him what William Phiri had taught me.

'That sounds like a reference to that old Odyssean character Sisyphus,' said Hugh. 'He was condemned to push a great boulder to the top of a hill, only to have it perpetually roll down again.

'Isn't that a metaphor for human life?' I asked.

★ ★ ★

There was still no sign of the bus and I could see a man nearby looking at his watch and shaking his head in frustration. It wouldn't help. I looked away and then something happened that I will never forget. There was a gap between the upper and middle branches of the *Ziziphus*, and through it I began to make out something white against a darkening, blue-grey sky. It took me a few seconds to realise that it was snow and that something huge was hiding behind the 'tree of life'.

'My God!' I exclaimed loudly and then, through a tight mouth, I whispered to myself, '*that* is Kilimanjaro … not the other one that we saw from the aeroplane.' It all began to sink in. We had been looking at Mount Meru, Kilimanjaro's little sister, shorter in stature, different in temperament and, as I learned later, well worth climbing.

That tattooed man on the plane, the one who sat behind us – where was he? He did not know what he was talking about. I thought of trying to find him to correct him, but I knew he would have an instant answer to the mix-up. I figured there was no way that someone like that would admit he was wrong. I decided to leave him alone. Right then, I was far more interested in feasting my eyes on that incredible curving profile through and beyond the *Ziziphus* tree. There it was, the highest free-standing mountain in the world.

My eyes could not move from it. It was a long way away but it was big, very big, and it was beautiful. My stomach really gave me the message. I was daunted. It was a visceral message telling me in a strange way that I was coming home.

Nothing could have prepared me for what I had just experienced. I tried to savour the moment with all of my senses, holding the sound, the touch of the warm wind on my face, the sight of the flamboyant tree in full flower, the feel of the thorns on the *Ziziphus*, the smell of the dry season and the gut impact of an ancient volcano that was playing hide-and-seek. I remembered the feeling my father said he'd experienced when he first stood on the soil of Africa. It was as if he had come home.

Something in my blood told me that I knew this place. I could not shake it off. It was as if I had been here before. Africa does that. I sometimes wonder if it is a genetic memory … an ancient inner voice that says, *Never forget where you have come from*. It says, *Re-member your beginnings … your genesis*.

For a moment, looking up at the mountain was like looking at an undiscovered part of myself. Suddenly seeing the big mountain, the real one, was like seeing a signpost that pointed to a path into myself. 'I know that mountain,' I said to myself.

And then, just as suddenly, the mountain felt very distant from me. I didn't know it at all.

★ ★ ★

I thought about the postcard my father had sent me from Tanganyika all those years ago, the one from the highest and lowest places in Africa. It felt like yesterday. Not very far from where I was standing was the Great Rift Valley and the famous Olduvai Gorge. I had been told you could see it from the northern edge of the four-thousand-metre-high Shira plateau on Kilimanjaro. Turning to Jessie, I said, 'There's a valley on the other side of that mountain which was once the home of *Zinjanthropus*, arguably our oldest ancestor. She lived there about two and a half million years ago. It was only yesterday.' Was she a forerunner of human consciousness? I wondered. Could she reflect upon herself?

6

A FLOCK OF red-winged starlings flew overhead. Their calls were fruity and melodious. I watched them as they headed off in the direction of the Great Mountain. Meanwhile, Jessie had been watching me testing the thorns on one of the branches of the *Ziziphus*. They were sharp, especially the ones that hooked backwards. I examined my finger, noticing the indentation of where the point of the thorn had been. I figured it wouldn't take much pressure from one of those thorns to draw blood.

'Do you think the message in those thorns and the story of Genesis are connected?' she asked. There was a kind of mischief in her eyes.

'What made you ask that?' I asked, amazed at her observation. 'I was busy trying to make the link myself … remembering where we have come from with the *re-membering* of our genesis.'

★   ★   ★

Before leaving Cape Town, Jessie had introduced to me a facet of Genesis that had never occurred to me before. 'Try taking the story and the characters in it a little more personally,' she said. When I told her I was not really sure what she meant, she urged me to look at what was written as a possible metaphor for individual development, particularly our psychological development. She asked me to see the characters in the story as aspects of myself, that there is a bit of Adam and Eve, Cain and Abel and so on, in all of us. At the time, that was asking a lot from me. For a start, the Old Testament story had never really appealed to me. Not only did the Adam and Eve story seem biologically unsound, but I also had to deal with a long-standing resistance to religious instruction, a 'hangover', no doubt, from my schooldays. Genesis was a part of that instruction. Then again, there was my father, the memory of his funeral and his choice of text at his final service. I wanted to forget that. I had neither the interest nor the inclination to decipher any hidden meanings in the story of the creation or in the roles of its early participants. And yet, I couldn't escape that experience in the attic back home, my grandfather's inscription to his son, and, if I was to come to terms with those waves of anger which I had in some way attributed to my late father, I couldn't escape the role of Genesis in the resolution of that anger. After all, the book of Genesis was *missing*! It had to be re-membered, as my grandfather had put it. But something in me was missing, too. At a gut level, I knew this was true. I hardly knew myself. Something in me had to be re-membered. As irrational as it seemed, I knew, as I stood in that attic on that cold spring morning, that the missing pages of Genesis and that which was missing in me would be found, or not be found, on the slopes of Kilimanjaro.

Jessie's words still echoed … 'You might find Genesis on the way.'

'I know where you are coming from,' she had said, trying to soften my resistance to the Old Testament. She went on to say that she would have agreed with me in the past, but with time and her own need to explore the creation myths of the world, she had come to appreciate stories such as Genesis not so much for their content, but for the inherent *meaning* they had for her. That was something I liked about Jessie – she always spoke for herself.

'In other words,' she said, addressing my usual scepticism, 'I don't necessarily believe the stories are historical truths. What I do believe, however, is that they can have a profound psychological significance for you and for me, when we learn to understand the symbolic language of the text.'

I was trying hard to stay with her. Then came the break-through. Jessie put her hand on my chest. 'It's one thing to look at an event like the creation historically,' she said. 'To do this is to give the event a *fixed* place in time. Looked at psychologically or symbolically, however, the event then becomes contemporary. It becomes not only ongoing, it becomes *personal*.' I knew she was addressing something deep down in me, something hidden.

'So the creation is happening *now*?' I asked.

'In a way, yes ...' she said. 'You see, Hamish, to me, creation is more than just a happening, or an isolated event. It is also a phenomenon of pattern and process. It is ongoing at many levels ... genetic, physical, psychological, sociological ... you name it. I think everything carries a *pattern* of creation.'

I liked the notion of a pattern of creation. I also liked the idea of process, something moving and dynamic.

'So you don't believe in Adam and Eve as specific people in our history ... one man coming along and a little later, a woman?' I asked.

'I think we have to be careful not to get ourselves bogged down in concrete thinking. More than anything, perhaps Adam and Eve deserve a symbolic interpretation if they are to have any contemporary meaning in our lives. They have to be taken *personally*. Psychologically, they are regarded as the prototypes of human consciousness.' Jessie waited for what she had said to sink in. 'When it comes to consciousness, they are the representations of what is most primal in us. They represent the original god-makers in us, as Nietzsche might have put it.'

At the time I remembered thinking of Hugh and his fascination for Greek and Roman mythology. I had never thought of it in the way that Jessie had put it, but there was no doubt that he took the gods and goddesses of those ancient stories personally. He often quipped that there was a lot of Hermes, the Greek equivalent of Mercury, in him; that his love for the open road, for commerce and for the world's mavericks was a quality of that particular god which had gripped him. He once said there was a fair dose of Saturn in me, referring to my scientific scepticism and my conservative leanings. When I told him that he had painted a rather boring picture of me he replied, 'No … Saturn is only a *part* of you. Your very objection to Saturn's conservatism is the voice of Dionysus in you, the half-mortal–half-god of ecstasy.'

I reminded Jessie of Hugh's attitude toward the ancient deities and how, in them, he saw gods with a human face.

'I suppose you would say that is what Genesis is about,' I suggested.

'Yes, I suppose I would.'

There was nothing for me to say. Jessie had left me with much to digest. Consciously or not, she had begun to tip me beyond my world of predictability, into a world of change, of seeing cycles within cycles. I was beginning to see myself in a world that was as restless in me as I was in it … an ongoing *Genesis,* as she had put it … a world in which the creation was still going on. For the first time in my life I began to take seriously the notion of a great genetic inter-linking of life forms … trees, animals and humans … that perhaps they had to be taken personally … *and it was good.*

Jessie put her arms around me and tucked her head into my neck. 'I want you to know something, Hamish. I take you very personally.'

★   ★   ★

Looking behind me, I saw Brian talking with the two American girls who were on the same plane as us. Near to them was the man whom I thought I knew from somewhere, the man that I did not like. He was talking to a group of people and pointing at Mount Meru with authority. It seemed that he was still in the dark. I wondered if he and I were in any way connected?

★   ★   ★

At last! A medium-sized bus, about a twenty-seater, limped awkwardly around the traffic circle in front of the airport building. I was not sure whether it was the entire body of the vehicle or whether it was the chassis that was twisted, but it moved rather like a crab, slightly side on.

When it came to a standstill, a plump, uniformed African lady disembarked. She announced that the bus had come to collect all the passengers travelling to Keys Hotel in Moshi. That was us!

She gave a broad smile and said she was sorry that we had to wait so long. They were late because they could not find the usual driver of the bus, which meant they had to find another one. She pointed to the man behind the wheel, introducing him as Moses.

How apt, I thought. I was sure that he was aware of the origin of his name, but I wondered if he knew of its association with Genesis?

There were at least thirty of us waiting to board and I wondered how we were all going to fit in. And of course, there was our baggage.

Moses was not at all phased. Whistling away to himself, he climbed up onto the roof of the bus and called for the baggage to be thrown up to him. It did not take long but I was pleased that we had no breakables in our main bag. I decided to keep my backpack with me. Its contents were too precious to let out of my sight.

With a thin, blue nylon rope, the driver tied the cases and backpacks onto the roof-rack. It looked as if he had done this many times before and the luggage seemed quite secure.

Jessie was already in the bus, keeping seats for Hugh, Brian and me. The American girls found themselves places in the back row and when I boarded the bus I could hear them talking to each other at the top of their voices. Brian told us that they were old school friends who had met up for the first time in about six or seven years. One of them lived in Seattle, the other in New York City. However, they had both grown up in Chicago, where they attended school together. To come to Africa was something that they had often spoken about and they decided the best way to start was to climb Kilimanjaro. 'They're bloody brave,' said Brian.

I wondered how many other people in the world had a longing to come to Africa?

The man I did not like got on board. He stopped next to me and after a long look, he said, 'Don't I know you from somewhere?' Searching his eyes, I shrugged my shoulders and then he put out his hand. 'I'm Lucas Steyn,' he said with confidence, firmly gripping my hand as he introduced himself.

'My name is Malcolm … Hamish Malcolm,' I said.

'Malcolm, sounds familiar. Maybe I'm getting you mixed up with someone who looks like you,' he said.

'Maybe,' I answered. His friendliness threw me a little and, for a moment, I warmed to him.

'Have you seen Kilimanjaro?' I asked him. I didn't wait for him to reply but pointed through the window next to Jessie to the white-domed mountain in the near distance. The sun had set, but in the twilight you could still make it out. Lucas Steyn bent his head and looked to see where I was pointing.

I watched him purse his lips when he recognised the mountain. Then came the frown. He nodded his head and said, 'That's it, okay! A piece of cake, hey?'

Lucas Steyn squeezed himself onto a seat toward the rear of the bus. I could see him staring into the fading light outside. The look on his face said it all. His eyes fixed on the mountain, his frown could not straighten itself.

★   ★   ★

As we boarded the bus, Hugh said something that I will never forget. It was as if he had picked up on my wrestling thoughts. '*The oracle at Delphi on Mount Olympus does not speak clearly, but it does not mislead,*' he quoted. For a moment the wrestling in my head stopped. For a moment, everything came together for me. Hugh could have been talking about Kilimanjaro, which he probably was, but he could also have been talking about the *Ziziphus* … it too, was an oracle. It too, when its message was taken seriously or *personally*, did not speak clearly, but did not mislead. He could have been referring to Genesis. As far as I was concerned, it too did not speak clearly and as for it being misleading, would that not depend on how personally I took it?

Despite everything that was going on in my inner and outer world right then – lugging my father's ashes around, toting an old bible toward a mountain top, discovering new metaphors for my life – I didn't feel misled. On the contrary, it all seemed to be leading somewhere … and it was good. It was as if Mount Olympus, Genesis, Kilimanjaro and the *Ziziphus* were oracles of their own kind. I was on a bus to somewhere.

★ ★ ★

Jessie later told me that not only do we have physiological instincts, but we also have psychological instincts. These instincts, or archetypes, as they are sometimes known, are the modern equivalents of the mythological gods. They have one thing in common, she said – they love to play hide-and-seek. They are always there but you have to look for them. When they speak, they mostly do so in our dreams and our fantasies. They hide in those strange, so-called 'coincidences' in our lives. They are in the essence of our anecdotes, without which our lives would be dry. Their speech is often cryptic but, like the oracle at Delphi, they do not mislead. '*Our physiological instincts are associated with survival,*' she said. '*Our psychological instincts are associated with meaning.*' After a while she added, 'To me, religion is a psychological instinct.'

7

SOME PEOPLE SAY mountains like Kilimanjaro are 'a piece of old cake', no great sweat in the climbing stakes, mostly boring and not one to repeat. Been there. Done that. These people are called *ego* climbers. When I hear comments like that, I wonder which part of them is doing the talking? How much of it is defensive, how much bravado? How much of it is a statement about their own lives … boring … unrepeatable? I suppose life can be like that – tedious, one step after the other, one breath in, one breath out, a 'what was that all about?' kind of life. There are other ways of seeing and acknowledging this mountain, however. Maybe, as my father had cautioned: you are not climbing it, it is climbing you! Maybe it is part of a dream and then again, maybe the mountain is dreaming you. I am not sure. I am not so sure of a lot of things, these days. Thinking about the mountain made me look at it again. I could still see it against the cloudless, dark-blue sky.

'She really is huge,' I said to Jessie, cupping my hands on the window to prevent the light inside the bus from interfering with the view.

'Why is it that most people refer to mountains in the feminine form?' I asked Jessie. 'I mean, we use words like … she, her, big mother, granny, old girl, bitch, witch. You don't hear people saying, "There *he* is, big daddy, big dog …"'

'Maybe it's because of what mountains represent in us, that they carry the feminine label,' she suggested. 'It's an emotional association, I think, something that is both daunting and beautiful at the same time.'

'Go on,' I urged.

'Well, when it comes to emotions, no one can pull the strings like a mother, especially our first one, our biological mother. Through her, most people learn what it is like to be on the *receiving* end of a god. That can be quite emotional, experiencing the first inklings of a creator, the one who holds you and then abandons you, the one who is happy to watch you stretch your wings, as long as you don't wander too far.'

'The one who says whatever you do you must speak to me about it first, you must ask permission?' I asked. Jessie nodded.

'It's true. Mountains are like that,' I said. 'Waving you goodbye with one hand, but pulling you back with the other ... like a mother and child.'

Jessie squeezed my hand, 'Do you know something ... when I first met you I thought you were a bit of a mommy's boy. Exactly as you are describing that mountain.'

'Really?' I asked, surprised and feeling a little hurt.

'Don't be hurt,' she said, 'you've come a long way.'

'Is that supposed to make me feel better?' I retorted. I remembered her saying something about Genesis and the task of leaving the mothers and fathers.

'Hamish! Listen to me. I was a mommy's girl for a long time, believe me. One day I saw her for who she really was ... a little old lady. I'll never forget it. I was free ... Well, as free as I ever will be of my mother's whims and ways.'

'But your mother's dead, Jessie. It's easier for you.' I was partially admitting to my own mother's influence over me.

'No ... it's not necessarily easier when a parent is dead. Sometimes the hold they have on us is even greater when they are gone. You're lucky, Hamish. Your mom's alive. You still have the opportunity to see her for who she *really* is ... that any hold she has on you is a result of who you *think* she is. Sure, there is something of a goddess in her, like in all mothers, but she is not *the* goddess. It would be unfair on her to expect her to be so. She is human. Think about it. Have you not done the same with your father? Remembering him as something of a god? Where do you think all those waves of anger came from, after each time you had spoken about him? You've never spoken negatively about him at all, have you?'

I didn't answer.

'Gods and saints are impossible to live with, you know … and even though I never knew him, I bet he wasn't a saint. Behind the scenes, I bet he got pissed off with people every now and then, as you do. I wonder if some of your anger is linked to some of his? Maybe part of it belongs to him. If so, you have to give it back, Hamish. It belongs to *him*. Sooner or later, we all have to look our gods in the eye.'

I did not know what to say. In fact, I did know what to say, but I did not know how to say it. I wanted to say, 'You're right.' Not because I knew it, but because I *felt* it.

'Hey, let's try and see the mountain through new eyes,' Jessie suggested, picking up on my silence. 'Tell me what you see now when you look at *it* … not at her or him?'

I looked hard and as dispassionately as possible at the fading snow-capped massif.

'I see a snow-capped elephant,' I announced with a deliberate, silly look on my face.

'And I see a great frozen breast, like my mother's,' she responded, bursting into laughter with me.

★   ★   ★

'About our projections,' said Jessie later, 'the serpent of Genesis is more than a symbolic penis. The apple or the fig are more than just representations of breasts. Old Freud may have got a few things right, but not everything that sticks out is a phallus and nor is every hole a fanny.'

8

WITH THE CABIN lights in the bus turned on I found myself staring blankly out of the window, waiting … as the rural people of Africa wait. I focused on Jessie's reflection and wondered what life would be like if she were not with me, if she had died, perhaps. I would be pretty lonely, I thought, interpreting the wave of melancholy that spread itself downwards into my chest. I didn't want to make out that I had some kind of perfect relationship with Jessie. Far from it. What I could not deny, however, was that in spite of our ups and downs she was a soul mate. It was something visceral. It was good to be having this special time with her.

I then turned my head and looked at her, at the woman who was part of my fate.

My backpack was on the floor, between my legs. I ran my hand over its contours, feeling the smaller bulge in one of the side pockets and a larger bulge, the one with the ashes, in the other. A thorn from the branch of the *Ziziphus* protruded through the canvas material of the pocket with the ashes. It was the thorn that hooked backwards: *Never forget where you have come from.* Opening the pocket, I readjusted the branch.

Mentally digesting the impact of the mountain, I remembered what my father had said about the geography of medicine and about homesickness … that each one of us has to discover our own medicine in life and that this medicine was not simply a chemical formula. It was an essence, something intimately linked to each person's history as well as to his or her geography … that there were certain places in the world where that 'medicine' worked best. Thinking about his first few moments in Africa, when he *knew* that he had come home, I now understood what he meant about the geography of healing. He once said, 'If you fail to consider the personal history and geography of a person's illness, then you will fail to understand the nature of one of the most undiagnosed of all illnesses.'

'What illness is that?' I had asked him.

'Homesickness,' he answered, looking deeply into my eyes to see if I had understood what he was trying to say.

Even though I could not grasp what he had said, something inside me at heart level told me the essence of what he was saying was true. I think I now know what he meant, mainly because I can speak for myself. I have come to see homesickness as another name for depression, the kind of depression that does not respond to medication. It has a geographical cure. Some people call that cure 'walk about'.

My thoughts went back to Eve … Adam's soul mate … how critical she had been in his fate, rescuing him from his 'father'. I thought of my own father and why I was sitting in that old jalopy of a bus in Tanzania. What role did Jessie have in possibly rescuing me from my father's hold, coming to see him for what he was, not for what I wanted him to be? Was Jessie something of an Eve? Was I something of an Adam? I told Jessie what I was thinking. I told her that in a different way from our children, she animated me.

'Did you know that the word *animated* comes from the Latin word *anima*, which means *soul*?' she asked. 'And so does the word *psyche*, named after the Greek goddess of beauty, the wife and lover of Eros. She was Eros's soul mate,' she added.

'Hmm … as a psychotherapist would you also call yourself a 'soul therapist'?'

'Yes, I try to be,' she said. 'When you are fortunate enough to learn what it is that gives individuals a sense of meaning in their lives, then you can begin to discover where their soul is.'

'And the phenomenon of a soul mate?'

'That's quite complex but essentially it describes that depth of feeling or animation that one person has for another … that without the one the other would feel that a big part of himself or herself was missing. It's a *shared* thing,' she emphasised. 'Of course, this can be pathological,' she continued. 'For instance, where a woman allows herself to be put on a pedestal by a man, adored for what she represents rather than loved for who she is, she then unconsciously carries his soul. This not only diminishes her, it diminishes him.'

'Are you and I soul mates?' I asked tentatively.

'Yes … I believe we are,' she answered. 'You animate me enormously. Without you I don't think I could have become a therapist. I had given up on any further academic training, as you know, but it was you who, to use your words, sparked the energy in me to go on. You made me believe in myself. You are a part of me, Hamish, and besides I feel as though I have known you for about two million years.'

'That's a beautiful thing to say,' I responded, and then after a moment or two of silence, I added, 'It seems we can't escape each other, Jessie. We can't escape our mothers and our fathers. We can't escape our mythologies, be they of Genesis or Greece, and we can't escape the fact that, right now, we're sitting in a third-world country in a third-world bus!'

It may have had something to do with our being in a strange country, far from home, but I could not escape the feeling of a different kind of rapport with Jessie. Through her I was beginning to think psychologically; in a way I was living in *two* worlds, one that was tangible, black and white, and another that was alive with symbolism … and meaning.

★   ★   ★

Sitting in that twisted bus, just letting things happen, it was as though I was beginning to find one or two threads in the twisting puzzle of my life. I had turned my back on my father's mythology, his gods and his God because I had been angry with *him*. To make sense of his life, it seemed I had to try to make sense of his death.

I looked once more at Jessie's reflection and then I looked beyond it. It was not *her* in the window. It was me, looking into a part of myself … into the heroines of Genesis and Greek mythology … the Jessie in *me*. Without that part of me, there would be no animation, no energy for a personal *Iliad* or *Odyssey*. There would be no reason for me being where I was. There would be no reason to *re-member* Genesis.

9

SUDDENLY, AMIDST A thick black cloud of diesel exhaust fumes, the vehicle came alive. Every available seat on the bus was taken and in some places three people had squeezed themselves into two seats. Two men, outside the bus, were shouting at the driver, who was struggling to hear them above the complaining whine of the engine. One of the men was pointing toward the mountain while the other was waving his arms in front of his face, trying to disperse the diesel fumes. The driver stood up and looked into the cabin, scanning the passengers and seats. He then leaned out of his window and yelled some instructions to them, pointing with a free hand into the bus. They excitedly ran around to the side entrance and climbed in. I did not know where they were going to sit, but I knew that somehow or somewhere, they would fit in. You don't have to be in Africa very long to witness the staggering number of people that can fit into a vehicle. In Mozambique, I was once part of a group of twenty-three people crammed onto the back of a van. No one complained of being uncomfortable. In some parts of Africa, if a vehicle can move, then it is roadworthy!

At last, we were on our way to Moshi. I could not believe that it had taken so much history, geography, mythology and psychology to get out of Kilimanjaro International Airport. A man wearing a tie and sunglasses and looking fairly official, manned the gate at the entrance to the terminus. He waved us through and called out something to the driver, who yelled back at him, his head and the top half of his body protruding from the window, precariously holding onto the steering wheel with one hand. They both laughed, shaking their heads, and the man with the sunglasses closed the gate behind us.

'These people all seem to know each other,' Jessie remarked.

'I was thinking the same thing,' I said. 'This is a land of extended families. In a way I envy them.'

The twisted bus threaded its way into the night.

★   ★   ★

'Listen to this,' said Jessie. She had been paging through a booklet on Kilimanjaro. I made a space so that Hugh and Brian could lean over the back of our seat.

'This had better be good,' said Brian, pretending to be serious.

'I think you'll like it,' she answered, not taking the bait. 'So will you, Hugh. It's a little piece of local mythology.'

'There is a legend among the people who lived on the slopes of the mountain. They say there was once a giant cow that lived in a cave which extended from the top of Kibo Peak into the glaciers and onto the south-facing slopes. The cow's name was Rayli.

'She was a great friend of the sun and it was because of this bond and the energy she gave to it, that the sun would chase away the clouds every year, bringing to an end the cold rainy season. Rayli was so big and so fat that, whenever she moved in her cave, she could only do it very slowly. From her tail, which hung down from the glacier, dripped a sweet-tasting butter. It was said that whoever put his lips to this butter, would develop supernatural powers. But it was not that easy. You had to ask permission to come to that cave and before you did that, you first had to make sure that your own house was in order, that you had done all the things you were supposed to have done, like paying your debts and making your peace with your neighbours. There was no point in trying to sneak up on Rayli.' Jessie looked up over the top of her spectacles at Brian. 'She could see you coming from miles away,' Jessie continued '... and even when she had her eyes closed, she could detect human footsteps as far down as the rainforest. Whenever she sensed that someone was approaching, she would let out a roar that sounded just like a lion, so loud and so deep, that it frightened the dreams out of sleeping warriors. Meeting her was not a task for the faint-hearted. For anyone who wanted a taste of that butter, it involved a two-way journey. It was one thing to climb to the cave on the top, it was another thing to come down again.'

'Like an *Iliad* and an *Odyssey*?' I asked. Hugh looked impressed.

'Listen to this addendum to the legend,' Jessie said, not taking her eyes off the book. 'Some of the local people say Rayli is still in her cave and that even today you can sometimes see on the faces of certain people who have climbed to the summit that old Rayli has given them a taste of her butter, that they have heard the lion. There are others who say they have been there, but you can read in their eyes and in their speech that they were nowhere near Rayli. All that they could do was complain about the cold. They were probably climbing on the wrong mountain.'

'Thanks, Jessie,' said Hugh. 'That butter sounds a lot like the forbidden fruit from the Garden of Eden, doesn't it? Interestingly, the old Greeks said that you could always tell if someone had been to Mount Olympus. There was something different about them. They had changed. There was a look in their eyes. Maybe they had tasted the "butter".'

I then remembered the story of the Italian prisoner of war in that last letter that my father had written to me. Like the stranger who came to our door … it was in his eyes. 'He did it!'

⋆   ⋆   ⋆

Jessie told me this happens in therapy too. 'Sometimes I've been fortunate enough to witness a profound change in a client. There is no doubt about it, a kind of healing has occurred. It's a moment that is indescribable, unpredictable and unrepeatable. There's something different about them … a look in their eyes that was not there before. It's as if they have been somewhere they had never been before.'

10

IT WAS STRANGE to think that we were in Tanzania when hardly twenty-four hours before we had been going about our lives on the southern tip of Africa, thousands of kilometres away. I had a peculiar sense of a time warp and I reached out for Jessie's hand to make sure this was all real. I was very aware that this was a special journey, not only an outer one, but increasingly, it seemed, an inner one … a journey that was taking me.

I thought about the nature and the significance of human journeys and it seemed to me that although I had not been aware of it before, there was always a concomitant inner journey, perhaps even more important than the outer one. What was not automatic, I began to realise, was the necessary task of experiencing both journeys *consciously*. Easier said than done. Paying attention to the inner paths was not easy. As paths of self-discovery, they were not mapped out. I had never been there before. Timing was important, it seemed. A lot of the outer stuff had to be sorted out first and, even then, I wondered if the inner journeys were for everyone? There was only one reason for me to be making this mountainous re-examination of myself: *I had no choice.* Jessie said that there was another reason, referring to her work with her clients: *a willingness to be disturbed.*

I remembered Yeats … *I went down into the hazel woods today, because there was a fire in my head.* 'Yeats had no choice,' I decided.

I tried to think of people I had known, who had gone into themselves because they had to. Jessie, I think, was one. My father, by all accounts, was another. I suppose my mother, too, was someone who had to come to terms with some of the twists in her fate. Hugh was yet another one of them. He had turned his back on an academic career to work in the Botswana wilderness … because he *had* to.

I imagined the task of going into myself as someone entering a great forest, familiar at the edges only. It helped to have a guide … to go with someone who had been into themselves, who could recognise the wild and unfamiliar inner paths in the psyche and who could bring you *out* again. I could appreciate what Jessie meant when she said that she could only go as far with her clients as she had gone with herself.

I glanced at the people sitting around me, their heads gently bobbing to the rhythm of the road. Some of them sat quietly. Others were chatting away. A game of cards was on the go at the back. Lucas Steyn had his eyes closed, while the American girls had found something new to talk about. I wondered what other journeys were going on in that bus?

★   ★   ★

'How are you two getting on?' I inquired, addressing both Hugh and Brian.

'I was thinking about the old gods of Greece again,' said Hugh. 'Apollo's admonitions would have been good advice for our climb. You don't have to listen to this, Brian. It gets a bit heavy.' Brian stiffened. I could see Hugh's remark had pinched him. Hugh saw it too and gave Brian a gentle punch on the shoulder.

'Remind us of them,' said Jessie.

'No! Allow me,' Brian interjected, catching the three of us by surprise. 'You think I'm some kind of moron, hey?' He looked directly into Hugh's eyes. 'How about these …

Honour the gods
Do no-thing in excess
Know thyself.

'How the hell did you know that?' Hugh took the question out of my mouth.

'I'm not that ignorant, you know,' he said, addressing Hugh with mock disdain. 'Knowing you as long as I have, *something* had to rub off!'

'Oh, so we have a dark horse in our midst,' Hugh responded.

'I could've told you that all along,' said Jessie.

'Shut up, all of you. Now it's my turn,' said Brian, 'but I am not going to be as longwinded as you guys.' The three of us involuntarily braced ourselves.

'To me, honouring the "gods" as you call them is about being *human*. It's one thing to imitate them. It's another to identify with them. Identify with them, and they will destroy you! If you want to booze like Bacchus, he'll kill you. If you want to fly like *Icarus*, then you'd better watch it … you're heading for a big fall! Maybe we humans are mortal because that's how it's *supposed* to be. All the talk of heaven and hell and what happens to us in the next life and so on is a waste of bloody time. Who cares? Don't you think our task while we are *here* is to be as *human* as possible and not to take ourselves too seriously.'

There was a warm yet tangible silence between us – none of us had heard Brian talk like this before.

'To do *no-thing* in excess, as if there was a hyphen, should not be interpreted as doing everything in moderation. That's boring. By all means be excessive,' he continued, 'but don't be excessive all the time!'

'I like that,' said Jessie. 'Me too,' I agreed. Hugh was quietly shaking his head. The wind was out of his sails.

'The last one of Apollo's admonitions, however, is the difficult one for me,' Brian said scratching his chin. '*Know thyself*. How the hell do you ever *know* yourself?' he asked rhetorically. 'Surely knowing yourself is an ongoing thing, a combination of uncovering different aspects of yourself and of learning others. Maybe it comes back to the other two admonitions … that to know *thyself* is to know also, the *human* condition and to *live* it to the full. I don't know who the gods are, or who God is, but what I do know, is this … it ain't me.' Warmed by what he had said, I couldn't help smiling.

'I think what you've said is spot on,' Jessie answered. 'So do I,' said Hugh.

'And your interest in Genesis, Jessie? Where does *that* come from?' Brian queried.

'It was part of my training as an analyst' she said. 'Understanding our cultural history is an important aspect of psychotherapy. As for the scriptures, we must remember that they are central to the Jewish–Christian value system into which we are born, and from which, whether we agree with it or not, we cannot escape. Looked at differently, however, Genesis is a process of initiation, rites of passage, unfolding sequences of growing up, limit-setting, rebellion and misbehaviour. It is a lesson for learning how to leave the mothers and the fathers, of coming to terms with betrayal and rejection – very contemporary stuff. In Genesis you have a mirror of many things that we have already experienced in our own lives … sibling rivalry, jealousy, labelling and lies. But, for me, there is something else about it which is often overlooked: within it is the inkling that the biblical God has a *dark* side … and that same God needs a *human* face. That, I believe, is our task, and surely … *that* is what honouring the gods is about.'

11

THE VOICE OF Bob Marley boomed out of the tape deck at the front of the bus. The speakers at the back did not seem to be working, but it didn't matter because the driver had pushed up the volume as far as it could go. His head swayed backwards and forwards to the beat of the music, or was it the beat of the bus? I wondered how often he had played that tape, because every now and then the music slowed down to a groan. Bob Marley, as far as I was aware, was one of the patron saints of *cannabis* and I hoped the driver had not completely identified himself with the musician.

In the headlights of the bus I noticed there were a lot of old Land Rovers on the road. Four-wheel-drive vehicles are essential in the rainy season, in these parts of Africa.

We drove through the village of Sanya and, just ahead of us, we saw two men desperately trying to pull a large, pink domestic pig across the road before it was run down by the bus. They were dragging it backwards by one of its hind legs and the poor creature, its mouth wide open, was squealing in terror, trying to get back from where it had come. The driver pushed down on the horn of the bus and without slowing down, he swerved to avoid the pantomime. He shouted something at the men from out of his window and they shouted back.

'That's a road hog!' I quipped.

Brian leaned towards us and said he knew exactly how that pig was feeling.

'That's what you guys are going to have to do with me. You're going to have to drag me up that mountain,' he said.

Hugh and I laughed. Jessie said it wasn't that funny because that was how she was beginning to feel.

'I'm serious,' she said to me. 'I really hope I'm going to be okay.'

I put my arm around her shoulder. 'You'll be fine.'

The gesture did not reassure her and she gave me a look that said, 'How the hell do you know?' I knew that look well.

'If it helps, and if you want me to be honest, then you should know that I'm also worried about how I am going to do on that mountain. But I'll be there with you,' I said.

★   ★   ★

'That's something I learned in therapy,' Jessie once said. 'You can't tell a client that everything is going to be fine. How do you know? It often doesn't work out that way at all. Sometimes, all you can do is to *be* there with the client.

★   ★   ★

If I had heard Jessie correctly, Genesis was emerging as both a story and an admonition to come out of a state of innocence into a greater awareness or consciousness of myself and the world that I lived in. In a way, hidden in its contents, were the principles of the ancient alchemists whose task it was to facilitate the process of transforming lead into gold. Seen symbolically, this meant transforming the leaden circumstances in my life into something of value, and in the process, getting to *know myself*.

In the light of my resistance to conventional religious systems, I began to see how much is lost when religions are concretised … when they become doctrines. Religion and theology it seemed were not the same thing. If religion was something personal implying an individual sense of connection with life, then theologies had become the concrete and collective *interpretations* of religion. It was the theological doctrines and not religion that people went to war about. It was the theological doctrines that invariably predisposed to the numbing not only of the individual spirit, but also of the spirit of religion.

Later, I told Jessie what I had been thinking. She agreed with me.

'I wonder how many religious leaders distinguish between spirit and soul?' she pondered. 'Did you know that, little more than a thousand years ago, the all-male council of the Holy Catholic Church decided that the word *soul* had no further relevance in modern scriptures? In their wisdom they decided that *soul* and *spirit* were the same thing? Think about it. They are not. Soul is essentially feminine — it animates, it implies warmth, moistness and creativity; it implies nurturing. Spirit on the other hand is essentially masculine. It is much more of a calling … a lone voice. Spirit has a sharp edge; soul is fluid. And we need *both*.'

'Why do you think the feminine movements have come of age in the last decade or so?' she added. 'I believe it's because something in the psyche does not forget. Soul will be *re-membered*.'

'We can throw the feminine out of theological doctrines, as you implied, Hamish, but we cannot throw it out of religion. Soul can't be forgotten.'

12

I HAD FORGOTTEN that it was Saturday night. The road was becoming increasingly busy and cars were intermittently passing us from both directions. I did not mind that, but what disturbed me was the narrowness of the road that made it a tight squeeze for two vehicles to occupy the tarred surface. The road was after all the main link between Arusha and Moshi and these were both very large towns. What made the road feel even narrower, however, was the fact that our driver seemed determined to keep our four-wheeled 'crustacean' on the tar.

From where we were seated, it looked like we were driving in the middle of the road. This was most disconcerting. All thoughts about soul and spirit began to vanish. Instead, my adrenal glands were on full alert. My instinct to survive was getting to be much stronger than any possible religious instincts.

Suddenly a car appeared up ahead, coming toward us with its headlights on bright. This made it difficult for anyone to see the road and I presumed that the driver was in the same predicament. Moses flicked the dim-switch a couple of times, hoping to give the oncoming driver the message. The message was indeed received and for a second or two the car had no lights at all. Dangerous. Barely twenty metres from us and closing in fast, its lights came on again, in full brightness, leaving our poor driver temporarily blinded. Within a second of a certain collision, it swerved past us, throwing up a shower of gravel from where it had abandoned the tar. From its otherwise silence I presumed that its horn did not function either. In the bus the only two people who were not fazed by what had happened were the driver and Bob Marley, who kept on singing.

★   ★   ★

And God said, Let us make man in OUR own image …

Plural? A father God *and* a mother God? Spirit *and* Soul?

I thought about the thorns of the *Ziziphus*.

And we are made in *their* image. A genetic plurality? The double DNA threads of a mother and a father God?

'Adam and Eve symbolise the original artists in us,' said Jessie, 'curving threads of god-making, as Nietszche may have called it.' I liked that. I recalled a conversation with Jessie not long before we set off for the mountain.

'Consider the pattern of Genesis in the development of human consciousness,' she had said. 'From childhood through adolescence and into adulthood, from no-thing to some-thing. First, we are neonates, flexed and floppy. As infants, tone comes into our bodies, the first resilience, the earliest physical readiness. We reach out, extending our arms and legs, our first exploration. We open up. Primitive reflexes are inhibited – no more rooting reflexes when our mother's nipple or finger touches our cheek. There are fewer panic reactions to unfamiliar sounds and jolts. We can roll over on our own. Our arms and hands begin to move independently. We reach out again. We can actively grasp. The world is at our fingertips and we begin to explore it. We transfer from hand to mouth. The world tastes strange. We smile and mother smiles back. Our whole world smiles back. It is a powerful mirror. We look for ourselves in our mother's eyes, and, like Narcissus who fell in love with his own image and fell into the pool of water, we fall into her eye.'

'Go on,' I said, 'I can see myself here.'

'In a powerful urge, the child rights itself,' she continued, speaking in the third-person. 'It pulls itself upwards. It can sit. It can support itself.'

Jessie switched to first-person speech. 'I stood up. Suddenly the world changed. It was a lot different from up here. I saw my mother and my father. They came and went. They played hide-and-seek. Would they ever come back? Maybe … maybe not.

'I learned to live with her and without her.' Jessie looked at me. 'Okay, it's your turn now,' she said. 'Begin with your schooldays.'

I cleared my throat. 'I'll try …' I said. 'I went to school. I began again. I was no one. Socially I was flexed and floppy, I was vulnerable, but I learned quickly. Responding to the tone of the place, I became more receptive and more resilient. I had to be. Mother as I knew her was not there. Now there was another mother. She had many children. I had many siblings. Automatic reactions had to be inhibited. Tears had to be dried. Mother was not there to run to. Time became different. My world changed … forever … no endless days … just endless hours … I had fully entered the world of the "other" … a world of adding up and taking away, *this*, more than *that* … *This* was worthy, the *other* was worthless. I made *mistakes*. My new mother, the teacher, asked me what was *wrong* with me. I was on my own … out of the "garden". There was a powerful urge to right myself.'

'Go on,' said Jessie. 'Let Genesis speak.'

'I stumbled into adolescence, a lot more child than adult. Who are you? I asked, looking at myself in a mirror. Whose body is that? I questioned, looking at the blemishes. I felt floppy and flexed in my adolescent awkwardness. The young artist in me righted himself, reaching out toward an adult world. There was a different tone and a different kind of resilience in my speech. There was a new shape to my body and a new restlessness in my belly. I asked new questions. Why was the world the way it was? Why was there such injustice? Who made the rules anyway? Who said I can or that I can't? Who said that I have to get permission?'

Jessie quoted from Genesis … '*Get thee out of thy country, and from thy kindred, and from thy father's house, unto a land that I will shew thee.*'

I pictured my first caesarean section as an intern. It was part of my initiation into the strange science of medicine. Gowned and masked, I was hot in the operating theatre. It was difficult to breathe. My heart was somewhere in my throat. I stood staring at the knife in my hand. The hugely curved abdomen peeped from a hole in the surgical drapes. I was suddenly catapulted back into the boyhood world of my father's stories, to the great caesarean section of Africa, to the place where a great water fell away from itself, leaving as a signature the ancient scar of the Great Rift Valley. Was it his finger that I could feel tracing the midline of my body, or was it a bead of sweat?

Awkward and insecure, I reached out for help which I knew was somewhere inside of me. There was a powerful urge in me to do it right. I was on show. Gathering my thoughts, I went through the sequence − cut, open up, examine, identify, confirm, deliver, repair, close up, care for the wound. I could feel my hand shaking and then I made my move … one life became two … *I was in a new country*. I could never go back.

Coming to Kilimanjaro, I was anxious, awkward … a stranger. I was reaching out to the mountain. Then I knew … I was on my own. I could not turn back.

13

THE BUS PULLED up outside the Keys Hotel in Moshi. In the parking bays were some expensive 4×4 Land Rovers and Land Cruisers. They all had animal safari logos painted on the front doors ... elephants, eagles, lions.

Tourism, especially the wildlife safaris, is big business in many parts of Africa today. It is mostly geared for overseas visitors from Europe, America and Japan. This is not because these people are more interested in animals than other tourists like us, but because they are the ones who can afford it. Payment for safaris is in U.S. dollars at U.S. prices. Unless there are local rates, these prices are out of reach for countless African people.

Money was not the only deterrent for those who had been put off by Kilimanjaro. It was cold up there. It was lonely at times. The altitude made it a physically gruelling climb. Sometimes you felt so tired and so ill that the thought of dying was not a bad alternative.

Jessie and I had decided not to let the exchange rate and the cost of this trip get to us. We knew more or less how much it was going to cost us. It was expensive by home standards but we needed to do it. We borrowed from our mortgage, but we figured it was only money.

I have discovered that some journeys just have to be taken, and you can't put a price on them.

★　　★　　★

Disembarking from the bus, I was drawn to the warm glow from the hotel lights shining through the flamboyant trees in the parking area. Although I could not see it, I knew the mountain must be close by. Suddenly I had another overwhelming sense of familiarity about the place. I had seen it all before. The glow and the image of the mountain nearby was a *déjà vu* experience for me. I *knew* the place. It was as if the mountain was waiting for me.

There were two ladies at the hotel reception desk who gave us a smiling welcome. They looked smart, dressed in the same maroon uniform as the one worn by the lady who escorted us in the bus.

Weary from the plane journey, the bus ride to Moshi and all my mental gymnastics along the way, I hoped I would not have to wait too long before getting under a hot shower. I was pleasantly surprised to discover the receptionists had been expecting us and our rooms had been organised. It did not take long to sign in and the lady who handed us our room keys asked if we were in Tanzania on business. Jessie said, 'No, we have come to climb Kilimanjaro.'

'You have come to climb the *mountain?*' she asked, sounding singularly impressed.

I felt pleasantly chuffed, puffed up with a kind of smug superiority, until I noticed her shaking her head and smiling.

'I wonder if she thinks we are courageous or crazy?'

Jessie peered at me from below raised eyebrows and whispered, 'She thinks we're crazy!'

'I hope you have a good stay in Tanzania,' said the lady diplomatically, without further reference to the mountain.

It was good to feel welcome. Even so, I wondered if we were being welcomed to the 'gates of hell'.

It was a warm night and the first thing I did when we entered our room was to switch on the overhead fan. We were lucky, because we learned that not all of the rooms had ceiling fans.

Our bedroom consisted of two single beds, which I pushed together so that they were positioned directly beneath the overhead fan. While I checked the cupboards and drawers, Jessie was taking a shower. I could hear her humming to herself. Great! That meant the water was hot. Stripping down to my underpants, I plopped down onto the bed nearest the open, east-facing window and closed my eyes.

★ ★ ★

… darkness was upon the face of the deep … and the spirit of God moved on the face of the waters …

I pictured the coming together of two twisting genetic threads, male and female. Then, a great dividing. One cell becoming two, then four, then eight, sixteen, thirty two, sixty four … and so on … then a pulse … a curving cord … gill slits … the divisions went on. In my *becoming*, water fell away from itself, membranes divided the extracellular fluids from the intracellular. The waters on the outer side of the membranes tasted of the rivers, the waters on the other side, of the sea. Already the journey from sea to river and then to land had been rehearsed. I began to take shape. I was a cell, a capsule in the amniotic fluids of a great mother. Suspended in her space, I turned over and over … I turned *into* her. It was dark. I heard a high-pitched whistle as if from a distant ancestor. My gill slits closed. Was it the call of a great whale on its way back to the sea?

I heard another sound pulsing through the waters … the beat of another heart … the first sound of my mother. She came and went with every beat. And then I heard her voice … it also came and went … the sound of kin … my belonging.

Bathed in her amnion, the scented memory of my mother was in my nostrils. Every perfume, every memory would be judged against this one. I would know her smell anywhere.

Therefore shall a man leave his mother …

I was being primed for the first of life's two great physical partings … birth.

★ ★ ★

Get thee out of thy country, and from thy kindred, and from thy father's house, unto a land that I will shew thee …

Nigredo … darkness … and then the flow. Following the waters of my mother, my body, like clay, was moulded and pushed headlong through a final passage of shadow, into the light.

And there was light!

Albedo … light! The midwife acted swiftly. One life became two. A cord closed forever. That which belonged in water, was now a creature of air.

I wanted to go back.

She cradled me in her arms and then gently teased open the blanket to look at my face. She was trying to smile. She spoke for a million mothers.

'Who are you?' she asked in silence.

'What is your name?'

'For how long have you come to stay?'

'Let me see your palm.'

'I know you from somewhere.'

I could smell her. I could taste her. She came from my world of darkness.

A tear threaded its way down her cheek. She wiped it away.

Slowly and very deliberately, she stroked my cheek and forehead with her finger. She made a sign, like a circle, on my forehead.

In sorrow shalt thou bring forth children …

I felt her skin. It belonged to me.

I tasted her. Her juices came from my own mouth.

She and I were one. I fed from her … she fed from me.

I saw circles of darkness before me … her mouth, her eyes, the areolae of her breasts … ancient circles … ancient windows into an ancient world.

I was held.

I was warm.

I was afraid.

14

I OPENED MY eyes to see Jessie standing close to me. She had come out of the shower, modestly pressing a small white towel against the front of her body with one hand. In her other hand she was clutching the shirt that I had been wearing and which she had picked up from the floor. I watched as she buried her face in it.

'What are you doing?' I whispered, catching her by surprise.

She blushed and then said to me, 'I love the smell of your clothes after you've worn them. I would know that smell anywhere.'

'You're weird and you're beautiful,' I said, reaching up for her and pulling her gently down toward me. Her towel fell to the floor revealing full breasts and an athletic body that was still wet from the shower.

I said a silent 'yes' to the powerful stirrings in my body. So did Jessie.

★   ★   ★

'Where the hell have you guys been?' Brian and Hugh asked in tandem. They were sitting in the lounge of the hotel. They both looked fresh and relaxed. Jessie's hair was still wet and she had pulled it back into a ponytail. There was a flush to her cheeks.

'We had a few things to sort out,' I said, not committing myself to the absolute truth.

'Let me order you guys a beer,' Hugh offered, tactfully changing the subject.

The hotel lounge and dining-room, a Spartan, open-plan design with split levels opening to the outdoors on two sides, was packed with locals, travellers and visitors. The dining area was on the lower level and its red polished floor had a shine to it. The chairs in the lounge were covered with an easy-to-clean plastic material. These had all been occupied and Hugh fetched two plastic garden chairs from the patio outside. No one seemed to mind. There was a buzz of Saturday night activity in the place.

A clicking sound was coming from the ceiling directly above us. It was from one of the three overhead fans in the lounge. A waiter who had come to our table to take our drinks order saw me looking up at the fan and said he was sorry, but they could not make it go any faster.

Listening to the clicks, I calculated that the fan was rotating at about one hundred and thirty cycles per minute. That was about the same as the heart rate of a new-born infant.

We ordered a round of the local draught beer because the bartender said it was the coldest he had. When it came, it had a good head on it and the warm air was already condensing on the outside of the tankards. We toasted each other 'good luck' and then we toasted the mountain. It tasted good and I could feel the cool fluid of the first sip making its way all the way down my throat, into my chest and downwards to my stomach.

In spite of the unknown physical task that lay ahead of us, we felt reasonably confident about our mental preparation to get to the top. We had all been told repeatedly that if we took it slowly it would be okay, but what worried us was the unpredictability of altitude sickness on Kilimanjaro. None of us had been at altitudes higher than four thousand metres before, which was apparently when most people started to feel the symptoms, which included headache, nausea, vomiting, shortness of breath and extreme fatigue.

Brian had us laughing when he said, 'That's exactly how I feel every Monday morning.'

I had read that at times the body's reaction to the high altitude could be a sudden and potentially fatal pulmonary oedema. This is an inflammatory reaction in the delicate inner linings of the lungs, causing them to become filled with protein-containing fluids. It is a serious condition because of the debilitating effect it has on the capacity of the lungs to exchange oxygen and carbon dioxide. Because it can happen so suddenly it it a matter of urgency that the person descend to lower altitudes as quickly as possible.

Hypothermia, the condition describing the loss of essential body heat, is another problem to be avoided. About this Hugh said, 'When your feet get cold, put on a hat!' That was good advice, because nearly one third of one's body heat could be lost from an uncovered head.

Brian had heard from someone that one in every three climbers on Kilimanjaro had to turn back due to altitude sickness and what was more, several deaths on its higher slopes had been reported in the past twenty years or so.

Jessie was silent, scratching her chin. She always did that when she felt stressed. She asked Hugh if she could have one of his ciga-rettes.

★   ★   ★

A waiter called us to dinner. He said it was getting late and the kitchen would be closing soon. He invited us to sit wherever we wished, which was an intriguing invitation – there was only one available table. The rest were occupied. He walked with us to our table that happened to be next to the two American girls. Leaning toward each other, they were still engrossed in conversation. Brian greeted them and they gave him one of those quick smiles of acknowledgement which said 'hello-goodbye'.

I was more thirsty than hungry, so I ordered another beer.

Jessie said we really should eat something because tomorrow was going to be a long day. Brian then teased her, 'Thanks, *Mom*,' he said.

'I'm not your mother!' she responded. 'You can do what you want. I was just thinking of all of you.'

Thinking back to our conversation on the bus, I grinned at her.

'Well, you will be happy to know that I am going to have some soup and rice. But, will you please cut my bread into little soldiers,' I teased.

Jessie shook her head and then punched me on my shoulder.

'Seriously, Jessie, do we ever leave our mothers?' Brian asked.

'Not really,' she responded. 'We have many mothers in our lives: grandmothers, aunts, teachers, institutions and so on. Schools, corporations, the civil service ... they're all mothers of sorts.'

'Do you want to know something?' It was Hugh picking up on the banter. 'My first marriage came adrift because, in effect, I'd married my mother. I became the eldest son in the family.' Brian looked at Hugh in bewilderment.

★　　　★　　　★

Close by there was a table with about ten people seated around it. They were young and all healthily sunburned. There were many empty beer bottles on the table and they were listening to a woman in their party who was making a speech. When she had finished, she raised her wineglass and toasted the group. Taking it in turn, each person had a say, each one raising a glass of beer or wine in a toast to themselves and to the mountain. The look in their eyes said only one thing ... '*We did it!*'

Two people at their table were quieter than the others. They were seated next to each other. The look in their eyes said ... '*Maybe another time.*'

There was a roar of laughter from their table and Hugh remarked, 'This time next week, that could be us.'

It was difficult to imagine. Next week seemed like light years away. My stomach knotted.

★　　　★　　　★

Brian yawned widely, only covering his mouth in the final stage of the exercise.

'Sorry, guys,' he apologised, 'I'm bushed.'

Across the room, the two American girls were approached by a man who had casually sauntered across the lounge from where he had been sitting with a group of his friends. With a bottle of beer in one hand and what I would find out was a rolled-up map in the other, he slowly negotiated the two or three steps into the dining section. I wondered how many beers he had emptied? With a graceful bow and a big smile he introduced himself to the two women. They offered him a chair and, before sitting down, he motioned with his hand for us to wait. 'I must speak to you about tomorrow,' he said.

Taking a swig from his bottle, he then cleared the salt, pepper and other condiments from the middle of the table, making space for his map, which he unfolded.

The map was a detailed one of Kilimanjaro, showing the contours, the various routes to the summit and the different levels of altitude.

With his finger he was indicating a possible route. The two women were listening intently, both of them cupping their chins in their hands. There were nods of agreement between the three of them and the man rolled up his map and got up to go. One of the Americans said something and I heard him answer, 'No problem.'

There was a big grin on his face and then he said, '*Pol-e, pol-e.*'

It was our turn after that and the man eased himself toward us. He was about thirty years of age, of medium height and his body looked like barbed wire, it was so tough and lean. He introduced himself as Julius and said that he wanted to brief us about the climb. We made room for him and introduced ourselves. He told us that he had been named after Julius Nyerere, who was the first president after Tanzania had become independent.

I wondered what his *African* name was. European names, since the first census so many hundreds of years ago, had lost their descriptive significance. African names, on the other hand, hadn't. I thought of my old friend William Phiri, whose African name was Ufikile … *the one who has come home.* He earned this name after his initiation into manhood.

★ ★ ★

Jacob of Genesis wrestled with his angel. It was the initiation of a god-maker. His name became Is-ra-el ... *the one who wrestles with God*.

Thinking about Hugh's astonishing statement, Jessie would later tell me that divorce had become something of an initiation for Western men. 'It happens that a man who leaves his wife, leaves his mother, also. For him, the event is often his "dark night of the soul" ... he wrestles with himself, with the calling of his family, with society ... he discovers what it means to be alone and frightened. The world will never be the same again. That's what initiations are about.'

★ ★ ★

I asked Julius if he would like another beer and he indicated that he still had enough in the bottle that he was holding. He took a sip and cleared our table so that he could unfold his map.

He showed us three possible paths, but recommended the Machame or 'whiskey' route. It was very beautiful, he said, and there were not so many people on it at any one time. This was music to our ears, because we had heard the 'Coca Cola' route could be quite crowded. The whiskey route was more difficult than the other because it was steeper and we would have to be careful on the glacier. 'No problem,' he concluded.

Whenever anyone says 'no problem' like that, with such confidence, I am immediately sceptical. Someone once told me confidence is the feeling you have before you have fully understood the problem.

My stomach started talking to me again. I was excited. I wanted to get going.

'There's one very important thing I must say to you. It is this,' said Julius, speaking deliberately and slowly. '*Pol-e, pol-e.*' We all knew what he meant.

Julius was laid-back. I liked him. I was impressed with his command of the English language and his self-assurance. I had taken an instant liking to the man. In a matter of moments that would change. Hugh asked him if he was going to be our guide. Scratching his head as he thought of how to answer – he didn't want to offend us – he said, 'No. I will be taking the two ladies and the people from Switzerland at the other table,' gesturing toward them. 'Thomas will be looking after you.'

'Oh,' Jessie sounded disappointed. Like me, she had begun to invest her trust and energy in him. 'Well, is he good … I mean, is he experienced?'

'He was my teacher when I was learning to become a guide. You will like him. He knows the mountain very well.'

A part of me wondered cynically if Julius was taking the Swiss and the Americans because of the possibility of higher gratuities. He would know the difference in value between Swiss francs, American dollars and South African rands.

Thomas might be lucky to have us, after all, I thought. I was feeling a little rejected.

Jessie beckoned to the Americans, inviting them to join our table. Their names were Carol and Helen. They were both attractive women in their twenties. Helen was a recent graduate in political science. She was taller than Carol, who had closely cropped blonde hair that stuck out in places.

After a round of drinks Jessie said that she was ready for bed. This was a welcome signal for all of us. I think everyone was weary. It had been a long day. Carol and Helen left us, as did Julius, who said he was going to join his friends in the lounge. 'Thomas will be at the hotel tomorrow morning. You'll like him,' he said.

As he left, Hugh asked him what the name Kilimanjaro meant. Julius thought for a few moments and then said, '*The journey that has no ending.*'

'That's life,' said Hugh, nodding his head. 'The never-ending journey – the fate of Sisyphus … pushing that boulder up the hill … never-ending stuff.'

I thought about the two rows of thorns on the *Ziziphus mucronata* … to be pushed and to be pulled …

As we were leaving the dining area, Lucas Steyn arrived on his own. He looked hurried and found himself a seat. The headwaiter approached him and before long Steyn was arguing with the poor man, who was looking at his watch, trying to tell him that the kitchen had closed. Steyn pointed at his own watch and finally the waiter indicated to him to sit down. He was a bully, I concluded. He had bullied the waiter into keeping the kitchen open.

Jessie and I ambled our way up the stairway to our bedroom.

15

THE SECURITY LIGHT in the car-park outside our first floor window illuminated the bedroom so that Jessie had to pull her sheet over her head to make it darker. It was warm. 'Thank heavens for the fan,' I muttered.

I had brought my own pillow with me from home. It was a soft down one which I moulded into the side of my head. You can't do that with foam pillows.

The fan made a soothing sound but that was about all. The cool breeze that I was hoping for was, at most, a gentle disturbance of the air. I wondered how Hugh and Brian were getting on. I turned around in my bed to face Jessie and saw that she was sound asleep.

Lying on my left side, I could hear the large fruit bats flying around outside. They made a metallic noise that sounded like a blacksmith's hammer beating against an anvil. Unlike other bats that are blind and use ultrasonic sounds to echo-locate, these fruit bats can see. Their high-pitched calls are said to be communication signals to their species. I could picture them feasting on the ripening mangoes in the trees in the hotel car-park.

Lying on my right side, however, I could pick up few sounds outside of a low-frequency range. I thought back to when I first became aware of my 'deaf' ear and with it, the onset of the tinnitus that sounded as though a thousand seething cicadas had taken up residence in my head. I had grown used to it.

I could make out the sound of dogs barking in the near distance. I wondered if they were barking at the moon, which was about four nights away from being full? Maybe they were barking at Rayli, the huge cow that lived on the mountain.

From the bed, I could see my rucksack in a near corner. I could just make out the bulge in one of the side pockets. I thought about the forward-pointing thorns, the ones that say you are on your own, keep moving, keep looking ahead. And then there were the other ones, the ones that hooked back ... the ones that say *pol-e, pol-e* ... take it slow ... never forget where you have come from. The thorns represented the complementary opposites in our lives, the paradoxes and the tensions that go with being pushed and pulled. We need both forces. We need the tension. Is that not where our creativity is born?

Then it struck me ... *fate* and *destiny*, like spirit and soul, were not the same thing. If *fate* was our allotment or our portion in life, then what is it that we give back to, or *re-member* about our fate. I could think of no better word than *destiny*. Destiny, it seemed, like soul, is what we give back. And then I thought about the thorns. One of fate, one of destiny. One of spirit, one of soul. For the first time I began to understand what it meant to have one's destiny in one's own hands. For the first time I began to understand the notion of giving the gods, those great spirits of fate, a human face. How I *re-membered* my fate, was up to me.

'Jessie!' I whispered urgently. 'Fate and destiny are not the same thing!'

'Hamish, please get some sleep,' she grumbled, changing her position and laying her outstretched hand across my chest.

16

It was dawn in Moshi. First light. Kept awake by the *Ziziphus* thorns in the dark hours of the night, I was pulled out of my scattered sleep by the distant call of Islam echoing through the room. It was the holy month of Ramadan in the Muslim calendar and the crier in the mosque tower was calling the worshippers of Allah to come and pray.

Outside, the sparrows had begun to chirp and from the window next to my bed I could see them pecking and hopping around outside the hotel kitchen.

The sun was nearly up. It was a soft light and I figured that I could get some good early-morning shots of Kilimanjaro. The best light for taking photographs is in the morning and the late afternoon. Hugh, who is a very good photographer, says you can't beat the late-afternoon shots. The light has a mellowness to it, which is absorbed into the subject. Early-morning light, on the other hand, unless you really catch it at the right time, is more of a reflecting light.

Jessie had often told me that for her the early morning was the best time to reflect. It was usually the best time for her work with clients. In the early morning the *persona*, that mask that all of us present to our world, is not as tight fitting as it usually is during the business of the outer, working day. Also, our usual ego defence mechanisms of denial, blame, rationalising and so on have not fully established themselves. At that time of the day the images of our dreams, our night speech, are like fresh tracks into the wilderness of the psyche.

Jessie was still clinging to her pillow. Wisps of her blonde hair lay randomly across her face and shoulders, adding to her sensuousness. I leaned over and whispered to her that I was going outside to take some photographs and she mumbled something about seeing me later. I put my pillow onto her chest and like a closing sea anemone, she pulled it down over her head, covering her ears and eyes.

Outside, the air was fresh and cool. There was a thin, high-spreading cloudbank to the east and the early-morning sun transformed it into a broad sheet of gold. Silhouetted against the illuminated sky was a grove of tall Australian eucalyptus trees, also known as blue gums, and on the side branch of one of them, looking as though it was growing out of it, was the dark outline of a roosting marabou stork. Through the lens of my camera I captured the stork in a latticework of zig-zagging branches and sky.

I saw another marabou circling above the hotel and then two more. I soon discovered why they were there. There was a dump-site directly in front of the entrance to the hotel, on the other side of the road. It was a shallow pit into which the daily vegetable and animal trimmings from the kitchen were thrown. In a matter of minutes there were at least five marabous in and around the pit.

The marabou, *Leptoptilos crumeniferus*, is a huge bird with a bald head and a massive bill. A large air sac hangs from the angle between the bill and the neck of the adult bird. This sac is inflated as part of sexual and territorial displays. Their long legs are strikingly white, the result of calcium carbonate rich faeces. These great birds defecate on their legs as an insulation measure, to keep them cool as well as to protect them from the harsh African sunshine. The marabou, like most vultures, are Africa's feathered scavengers of game kills, but they quickly discovered that where human beings go, waste goes, and they extended their clearing-up habits to human refuse dumps and abattoirs.

By human standards, the marabou stork is unbelievably ugly. Of course, the marabou does not think so. When we begin to give birds and animals human qualities, then the poor marabou does not have a chance. They become easy targets for human projections. I mean, who would want to be identified with a marabou? After all, they are ugly and they are scavengers ... the sort of human characteristics that we find extremely difficult to accept in ourselves.

When seen differently, there is something else about the marabou – in flight, they are among the most beautiful of birds.

To the north, basking in the morning sun was another beautiful sight. It was Kilimanjaro with its snow-capped dome, hiding once more behind the flamboyant trees that lined the gravel road outside the Keys Hotel. Red against white.

Holding the image of the mountain in the lens of the camera, I once again experienced the sudden sense of distance between me and it. I saw it as something utterly different from me, foreign and almost hostile in its silence. I felt as though I was on the edge of a tangible, critical distance, a critical space between it and me. To enter that space meant not only having to ask permission to do so, but first to honour its indifference; not to pretend that I understood what the mountain was about or to believe that it had any wish that I should enter.

And so, on that crisp morning, I asked permission from the silent mountain to know it and to be known.

17

AND HE MADE coats of skins and clothed them ...

According to the list of things we would need on the mountain – thermal underwear, head-warmers, gloves, gortex boots and jackets – the four of us were well prepared. Into one of the deep pockets of my backpack, I packed a first-aid kit that I had prepared in Cape Town. It was a blue canvas bag that contained two vials of diuretic, one vial each of cortisone and morphine and a litre of intravenous dextrose water. These were emergency medications and I hoped I would not have to use them. In addition, I had brought along capsules of tetracycline, homeopathic arnica, paracetamol tablets and a few anti-inflammatory agents, as well as a jar of petroleum jelly and a tube of sun-block lotion.

In the pocket next to the first-aid bag, I carefully packed the containers holding the ashes and the small, weather-beaten bible with the pages of Genesis missing, and the thorny branch of the *Ziziphus* tree.

Thomas, the senior guide Julius had told us about, was waiting for us in the hotel lobby. I immediately liked him. He had a gentle manner and smiled readily. A good-looking man in his late thirties, he was slimly built with high cheekbones that complemented what I would call a straight and noble nose. With occasional envy, I had seen photographs of Bedouin nomads with noses like that. There was a time when I would have given anything to have such a nose, in spite of my mother's reassurance that I had a nose that suited my face. An adolescent at the time,

I was not much helped by that kind of reassurance. I wondered how much of the adolescent was still left in me. The creases at the edges of Thomas's eyes, presumably from laughter or from years of squinting into the glare of the snows of Kilimanjaro, had been there for a long time. They were grooved and deep.

It did not take long for him to have our backpacks and sleeping-bags loaded onto the Land Rover that was taking us to Machame gate, the beginning of the 'whiskey' route. The engine of our vehicle started up just as the receptionists were coming out of the hotel lobby to say goodbye and wish us well. One of them told Thomas to look after us and with a disarming smile he said to them, 'No problem.'

We were on our way. Brian, Jessie and I sat in the back of the Land Rover while Hugh and Thomas sat up front with the driver.

We slowly rounded a traffic circle, passing a statue of a fierce-looking Tanzanian freedom fighter, a bayonet fixed to the end of his rifle and aimed at some imaginary foe. The road headed west, back onto the narrow Arusha highway that had brought us to Moshi the night before. We passed a row of leafy mango trees from which came the familiar sizzling sound of cicadas. That sound would always remind me of Africa, like the high-pitched call of the fish eagle, the grating *kek-kek-krrrrr* of the helmeted guinea-fowl and the long, curving whoop of the spotted hyena.

Hugh belched, blaming the cereal he had eaten for breakfast. He said it had tasted like cardboard. Jessie held her nose while Brian opened the window next to him.

I couldn't help giggling. I had a good feeling about our group. So did Jessie.

We turned north off the Arusha road onto a gravel one and, within a hundred metres or so, the driver had to change down to second gear to negotiate the upward slope. That's how we drove for the next five or six kilometres to Machame village, threading our way along a twisting dirt road that weaved through banana and pawpaw plantations. In some parts the scars of soil erosion had become too deep for motor vehicles to drive through and the Land Rover had to take a wide berth to avoid them.

Thomas seemed to be known to many of the people who were walking on the sides of the road. Many of them called to him by another name and he quietly waved back. So he also had his African name, I thought. I had a warm feeling for the man. It was as if I knew him too.

There is a phenomenon of Africa that always amazes me – the number of people you see walking or simply waiting along the roadsides, at any time of the day or night. I often wonder where they are going. Who or what are they waiting for?

There seems to be this incredible capacity of the traditional African to wait. It was not a part of my Anglo-African upbringing and I wondered who had got it right – them or me? A big part of me knew it was not me.

Most of the women on the road were dressed in brightly coloured caftans, many of them carrying young children, blanketed to their backs. An infant could not get much closer to its mother than that. I tried to imagine the significance of the bonding between the mother and the child, both of them being in such prolonged physical contact, both picking up the body warmth of the other. I imagined the security of being able to fall asleep to the rhythm of the mother's walk, to her voice, and from her back to look out onto an unfamiliar world with an increasing sense of the mother's eye.

Other women, with amazing ease, carried galvanised buckets and basins on their heads, most of which were filled with mangoes, bananas and other items in plastic packets. Some of them balanced large bundles of firewood on their heads, unconcerned about the weight of their loads. I saw no men carrying loads like that. Many of the men were smartly dressed in flannel longs and conservative white shirts. Some of them wore sunglasses. Most of them greeted us. They made us feel welcome.

The whining sound of the Land Rover in low gear was like the Pied Piper's seductive flute in that it drew to us, from the many side paths, scores of children who cried out to us in excitement, some of them sprinting alongside our vehicle, hoping for clothing or sweets or money. Many of them waved and called to us until we were out of sight. It was a warm and generous feeling. It didn't seem to matter if there was nothing that we had to give them right then. It was enough to be able to run with the vehicle, to shout and to wave at us. I have come to know that warmth and generosity as a very special feature of rural Africa. Another name for that warmth is *soul*.

I am often moved by a deep belief about the children of rural Africa, the ones that live down those side paths, off the beaten track. In spite of the lack of first-world possessions and, in some cases, having to endure unbelievable poverty, those children know what it means to *belong*.

I have learned that, for every one of us, personal trauma or tragedy is guaranteed. I think we all discover that at some time in our lives. It does not matter who we are, or whether we are rich or poor. What does matter is how we cope with it. We don't have to be psychologists to realise that those who are best equipped to deal with these traumas are those who from early on in their lives know what it means to *belong*. I wondered if it was this feeling of belonging that made so many of the African people of southern Africa as resilient and as forgiving as they are.

★   ★   ★

Enjoying the off-beat drive through the lush countryside, Brian told us a story about a New York taxi driver who was asked by a client why he had taken a round-about route? The driver responded, 'Refusing to go along an unfamiliar street, Mister, could mean that you are refusing a dance lesson with God.'

'He was referring to Hermes, the god of the open road,' said Hugh.

'In that case, I must have a lot of Hermes in me,' I responded. 'I'm always drawn to the side paths, the ones that wind off the beaten track.'

The winding footpaths and the children made me think of my Zambian boyhood and of William Phiri. We enjoyed the services of two domestic servants, one of whom was William. It is sometimes hard to believe that I used to live in a socio-political climate where it was acceptable to refer to these men as 'boys'. Maybe there was something in the African man that reminded the European about the forgotten child in himself, and that he did not want the 'boy' to grow up. The 'boy' had to know his place. The 'boy' had to keep his distance. Perhaps, it was more than that. Deep down and without being able to admit it, we were afraid, as Brian had suggested all those years ago. Afraid of what? Of being over-run? Of losing our 'standards' and our 'way of life'? Afraid of change? Afraid of losing our identity? How insecure can one be?

One evening I sat with William outside his *khaya*, watching him stirring his maize meal over an open fire. He preferred his traditional diet to ours. Sometimes, I did too. When the meal was ready, he placed the cooking-pot at the side of the fire and without flinching he scooped out a generous portion of the hot, ivory-coloured porridge with his bare hand. Moulding it and at the same time blowing on it to cool it down, he made a deep dimple with his finger at the one end. He then dipped the steaming handful of porridge into a saucer of gravy.

'Here, this is for you ... you must eat it. You are too thin,' he said.

I juggled the porridge from hand to hand until it had cooled down sufficiently for me to eat. It tasted delicious! It was a taste of Africa.

That night he told his usual stories about me ... the things that I used to do that made him laugh, the things he liked to remember me by. Turning to me, he confidently told me that I would be a doctor one day. It was written in my eyes, he said.

Children love to hear stories about themselves. It validates them. It gives them a deep sense of belonging. William Phiri knew that.

I asked him why white people called black people kaffirs? He shook his head, smiling, I think, at the frankness of my question. I was a boy.

'Maybe it was because they do not understand the black man,' he said thoughtfully. 'Maybe it was because the black man does not understand himself. Maybe the white man does not understand himself either. The white man has taught us many things ... but not many have asked us what we can teach them,' he said, ruefully. 'Here ... have some more porridge. We are talking too much.'

One day, I asked William if there was anything special that he still wanted to do in his life, and, without hesitating, he said, 'I want to go to the great mountain of my home.' He was pointing toward the north as he spoke, but I could see that his finger was slightly flexed, as if it was hooking back.

18

MACHAME VILLAGE, SITUATED on the lower edge of the vast rain-forest that circles Africa's greatest dormant volcano, was a hive of activity. In its centre there was a sloping field with an inevitable pair of makeshift soccer posts on it. Around the field were different kinds of food stalls, some of them displaying colourful splashes of tomatoes, mangoes, bananas, cabbages, pawpaws and sweet potatoes.

We pulled up directly opposite a butchery stall which had long pieces of meat and fat hanging from a line of wire in front of it. A young boy was waving flies away from the meat with a banana leaf. I pointed out the stall to Jessie, who is mostly vegetarian, and she gagged.

I told her that I had read somewhere that people who gagged easily were often susceptible to altitude sickness.

'Really?' she asked, testing me to see if I was serious. I just grinned at her.

Thomas pointed toward an uneven path ahead of us, narrower than the one we had been on, and said, 'We are nearly there.' Beyond and above the path was the ever-looming Kilimanjaro. I took a photograph of it with the food stalls in the foreground.

Thomas reached across the driver and pressed the horn a few times. No sooner had the last honk of the horn died, when someone came trotting across the field with a bag in one hand. He was holding a cap in the other. Thomas said, 'That is him. That's Julius. He is my assistant.'

Another Julius, I thought. There must be hundreds of Juliuses in this country.

It took another five minutes in the vehicle to wind our way up to Machame gate on the edge of the Kilimanjaro National Park. A freshly painted sign read 'Welcome to KNP'. There were a host of porters milling around the little wooden office in the official park area and it did not take long for Thomas to hand-pick the ones that were going to come with us.

We checked in at the office, writing down our names, addresses and passport numbers. The first two columns were easy, while the third was mostly blank. Few people had brought their passports. Ours were being kept in a safe at the hotel in Moshi. The warden in the office said it was not serious, but urged us to sign out on leaving, otherwise we would be presumed lost and they would have to come looking for us. We were given six days to get up and down.

'And on the seventh day shalt thou rest,' Brian quipped. 'See, I also know Genesis.'

Coming out of the thickets, Thomas had produced an armful of walking-sticks for us. He had cut them from the branches of some young trees at the edge of the forest. We all chose one for ourselves and in a salute to the mountain Hugh quoted from a Greek poem:

> I am but a bow in your hand, Lord;
> do not leave me, or I will rot.
> Do not bend me beyond my strength,
> or I will break ...
> but bend me beyond my endurance
> and let me break.

Stirred by Hugh's words and the looming mountain above us, I knew the theory was over. This was for real. Every cell in my body knew that this was going to be much more than an outer journey. It was going to be an inner one too, from a holding on to a letting go, from a going out to a going in, from the ego to the edge.

★   ★   ★

The Machame route began right there on the edge of the rain-forest. We were soon hidden by a canopy of dense leaves and overhanging branches. The dampness from the previous day's rain could be seen and smelt in the scattered leaves around us. So much for the dry season, I thought. Ahead lay a footpath that led us away from food stalls, flannel trousers and soccer fields … from Land Rovers and main roads.

I could see countless shades of green around me. Blue-green, grey-green, brown-green. Light. Half light.

The forest, flourishing between sixteen hundred and three thousand metres above sea level, seemed to know its boundaries. No higher, no lower. It was densely populated by huge camphor trees, different varieties of fig trees, yellowwood trees, cedars, palms, ferns, orchids, epiphytes, creeping vines and wild-olive trees. In a giant theatre, shafts of sunlight pierced the forest canopy, spotlighting in places the spongy carpet of leaf and moss.

And the earth brought forth the tree yielding fruit, whose seed was in itself, upon the earth. I could have been in the midst of that garden of Genesis.

A brilliantly purpled forest lourie, *Tauraco hartlaubi*, cawed in alarm as we entered its territory. It flew into the top branches of a neighbouring camphor tree and hid from us. A mountain greenbul called somewhere to my left, but I could not see it. It seemed to say '*sweet … sweet potato.*' It said it again. There was a lot of hide-and-seek going on in the forest.

I kicked away a moss-covered branch on the pathway. It looked like a dead branch, yet it was 'alive' with termites, flowers and fungi. I saw the 'dead' branch differently. I saw in it the cycles of the wild … death, decay and renewal … Order, Chaos and Order again.

The creation was going on in front of me.

86

I looked around, taking in the immense fertility of the place. I could imagine that every tree, every flower had once been a seed and every seed, by *necessity,* had once been in the dark, buried … out of sight. I began to see that the journey into oneself implied not only a willingness to work in the dark, but *with* the dark … that when something in oneself dies, something else comes to life.

And he planted a garden eastward in Eden; and there he put the man whom he had formed … the tree of life also in the midst of the garden AND the tree of the knowledge of good and evil.

Adam. The first man. Am I not the 'first' man in my world?

I saw two trees, one of spirit or fate; one of soul or destiny. I saw two rows of thorns.

★　　　★　　　★

A single beam of light shone through an opening in the trees, directly onto the path ahead of us. It seemed to say, 'This way, please.' The light was on my feet.

Looking behind me, I watched as Jessie stepped out of the shaded pathway into the sunlight. Her fair skin and hair, brilliantly illuminated against the dark-green background, gave the whole scene a sense of magic. Taking it all in, I allowed Julius, Hugh and Brian to pass me. Jessie soon followed and I stood there for a while, on my own. Thomas then appeared below me. I had thought that he was up ahead. He was carrying a bulging red backpack. Small beads of sweat had formed on the tip of his nose. He waited for me to get going and I continued at an easy pace, trying not to push myself. It was a decidedly uphill path, narrowly zigzagging its way through the forest. There were occasional short, flat stretches that I welcomed, stopping regularly, not only to take sips of rehydration fluid, but to take in as much of the surroundings as possible. It was a very special place. Whenever I stopped, Thomas stopped too. He said nothing, but quietly leaned against his stick and waited for me to start moving again.

'I hope I'm not going too slowly,' I said to him.

'No problem,' he answered.

I thought about something that Jessie had mentioned. When she was with a client, moving in and out of the boundaries of the unconscious, it was important to go at the pace of your client.

I looked at Thomas carefully. The man was *with* me.

★   ★   ★

I could feel a blister beginning to form on the outer side of my left small toe. It had been coming on for the previous hour or so, presenting as a slight burning sensation, exactly where the toe was pressing through the sock onto the boot. My initial thought was not to worry about it and that the irritation would go away. But it didn't.

Up ahead, the rest of the group had stopped for a rest and a bite to eat. Jessie took a packet of potato crisps out of her daypack and offered it around. Brian was the only one of us to say 'no'. Instead, he sat down and leaned against a tree. He looked a little pale.

I asked him how he was and he said, 'Fine.' Shortly afterwards, with his head between his knees, I heard him letting out a long sigh and at the end of it, a curse, 'Shit!' Thomas and I looked at each other without saying anything. We would have to keep an eye on Brian.

The blister had started 'talking' to me, so I took off my boot and sock to inspect it. The signs of the incipient blister were clear – there was a distinct red area of superficial inflammation. After covering it with a plaster, I smeared petroleum lubricant onto it and put my sock back on. I then found some broad leaves from a nearby bush and after smearing these with the thick lubricant, I placed them between my sock and the inside of the boot. With the extra lubrication the relief was immediate.

I thought about some of the irrational fears in my life that I wished would just go away, but refused to. They were like developing blisters. I could not ignore them. I had to face them and tend to them. I have learned that neuroses never go away. At best, they get smaller and less troublesome. I suppose Jessie would say that we have to learn to live with our psychological blisters.

'It's amazing how often it happens; whatever it is that you need most, is usually close at hand,' I said to Jessie, who was watching me dressing my blister. She had seen me using the leaves as added protection for my toe.

'It's as if the forest knew what I needed.'

She moved closer to me and waited until my boot had been retied.

'The psyche's like that too, you know. It brings you a dream when you most need it.'

★   ★   ★

Feeling rested, we were about to get moving again when we heard voices approaching us from below. We waited, and within seconds the shape of Lucas Steyn emerged from the foliage. He was in full stride, urging the rest of his team upwards.

Apart from a cursory glance at Brian, he ignored us completely. 'Come on! Come on!' he called out to his group, who panted and puffed their way past us. Their Tanzanian guide gave Thomas a whimsical grin as he passed him, shaking his head. We looked at each other with the same curious expressions and then Hugh said, 'What an arsehole.'

I was pleased that I wasn't the only one who felt like that about Steyn. Maybe it wasn't just a case of personal projections after all. He really *was* an arsehole. And no, I didn't *have* to like everybody. I felt good.

The bright shafts of sunlight suddenly disappeared, hidden by a rapid onset of cloud formation over the forest. It was getting toward late afternoon and high up on the mountain the ground surface had become markedly cold. This meant that the air above it cooled also. Meanwhile, the warm air in the lower reaches of Kilimanjaro had been rising so that the cold air from the higher slopes moved down to replace it, condensing into clouds as it did so. The reverse happened in the late mornings, when the cool air from the valley moved up to take the place of sun-warmed air on the heights, causing the summit region to cloud over. It was an ancient rhythm, an ebb and flow of warm and cold air, up the mountain in the mornings and down again in the afternoon, climatically described as an anabatic and katabatic movement, not unlike the anabolic and catabolic processes of human physiology – the body's biological feedback system of building up and breaking down, a kind of going out and coming in.

It began to rain softly and the sound of the droplets splashing through the forest canopy was like a soothing symphony of water, wood, leaf and earth.

Our group was walking in close single file. There was less chatter as the rain started to beat down. Fast-flowing rivulets formed on the path and we had to be more careful about our foot placing. I was at the front for a change, enjoying the silence from human voices, at the same time negotiating the puddles and the twirling root systems crossing the path, which I used as stepping platforms to keep my boots from getting too wet. They were supposed to be waterproof, but I did not wish to put them through any unnecessary test.

A message came through from Jessie, who was immediately behind me. She said we needed to stop for a while. It was Brian – he was not well. I looked back. He and Hugh had stopped. Brian was hunched up over his walking-stick and Hugh was talking to him. From where I was standing, I could see that he was decidedly pale, so I walked down the path to get a closer look at what was happening.

Brian said he had been feeling dizzy for the past hour. He was also nauseous and had a headache. He said it was a blinder. His speech was slow and a little slurred. I knew what he was going through. The last thing anyone wants to do when they are nauseous is to answer questions. You just want to have a good hurl, to lie down and sleep.

However, I needed to find out a few things, like: had he been unwell before he came on the trip, to which he said 'yes' … he had been on antibiotics for a recent chest infection. Why had he not told me, I wondered, trying to hide my frustration. Being on antibiotics could have explained what was happening with him, but my main fear, in spite of the relatively low altitude, was that he was showing the early symptoms of altitude sickness, hastened on by his recent respiratory problems. I figured that we were getting close to three thousand metres above sea level, and even though it was unusual to be symptomatic below four thousand metres, there were various factors like a respiratory infection that could bring on altitude sickness earlier.

The symptoms of altitude sickness rehearsed themselves in my mind – loss of appetite, headache, nausea and vomiting, shortness of breath, severe fatigue, pulmonary oedema, confusion.

I saw that Hugh was looking at me, searching my eyes and body language for some kind of reassurance. He did not find any.

Thomas was quietly watching the interaction between Brian and me. Removing his backpack, he strolled toward us and in a gesture of comfort, he gently placed his hand on Brian's shoulder. I was moved by what he had just done. He knew more about mountain sickness than me, having witnessed it so often. I knew the theory. He had *been* there. He had actually seen people die from it.

'Maybe in half an hour, we can stop at Machame camp,' he said. 'There we can rest. Tomorrow we can see if Mister Brian is better.'

Brian nodded his head. After a few minutes he said he was okay, and we slowly set off again.

★   ★   ★

A rustling sound in the thick canopy of leaves above us caught our attention. 'Look!' said Thomas, pointing into the branches. Moving its head from side to side, almost as though it were playing hide-and-seek with us, was a magnificent pot-bellied black-and-white Colobus monkey, *Colobus guereza*. It had a rounded muzzle and a characteristic protruding nose that hung down over its upper lip. It had a glossy black coat with a U-shaped mantle of long white hair on its sides, meeting across the lower back. Another part of the canopy came alive and two more of the primates appeared. One of them, a handsome female, was cradling an all-white infant in her arms. I focused my binoculars onto it and saw that the youngster had a pink face. It could have been human, I thought. The third Colobus approached the nursing mother from behind and began grooming her. Then, yet another monkey arrived, probably curious to see what was going on in the forest below. It was difficult to tell whether or not it was a male or a female, but it too began participating in the grooming session. Grooming behaviour is an essential part of bonding.

One monkey, possibly agitated by our presence, began calling in a rolling *rurr rurr rurr* voice and then the others joined in. Just then, one of them, whom I later realised was a resident male, made a spectacular leap, landing noisily on the branch of an adjacent tree, slapping it as it landed. Thomas told us that was its way of telling us we were in its territory without permission.

I can watch primates for hours. I love their hands and their arms, the way they reach out to touch and be touched. What really warms me to them are their eyes, particularly of the higher primates. Unlike many animals, the higher apes can engage with their human cousins through focused eye contact. The higher apes, like us, have well-defined facial expressions, for which the eyes are central. They can soften and harden like ours. They can reach out and let you in. They have the most honest eyes I know, and I do not think that is a projection.

As we moved away from the Colobuses, I thought about those people who would take exception to being linked to these creatures. To me, evolution was something beautiful. Being linked to the primates was a privilege. We could learn a lot about ourselves from them. In their own way they are god-makers.

The rain had stopped and there was a tangible silence in the forest. The path was muddy and I prodded the murky puddles with my stick, testing their depths. Suddenly, I saw a magnificent green snake slithering down the path in front of me. At first it seemed that it had not seen me, but then it stopped and raised its head, staring directly into my eyes. I stood still and watched it, fascinated by its apparent lack of fear for human beings. Or was it indifference?

My thoughts were racing as I made vain attempts to identify it. Was it poisonous or not? Who had the right of way here?

Not sure of its identity, I could not escape the notion that it was a young green mamba. This one was about five feet in length, sleek and in a capricious way, beautiful. Mambas have a venom that is toxic to the nervous system of their prey. It can be lethal to human beings.

The snake slithered slowly toward where I was standing. I felt my knuckles tighten around my walking-stick, but otherwise I did not move. Snakes are usually shy and sensitive creatures and it puzzled me that this one had not reacted in the way they usually do. Then again, that was how mambas often behaved. *You* were the one that had to get out of the way. The snake stopped again and raised its head and the forward part of its body an inch or so off the ground. I felt the build-up of an athletic tension in the muscles of my legs and arms as I held the ancient creature in focus. Maybe this one had never had previous contact with humans, but I didn't think it would have made any difference anyway, for it seemed to me that somewhere in the heart of almost every living thing there is an abiding suspicion of human beings. Even humans fear humans. It was not a pleasant thought. Watch out for human beings … they have a long history of being killers … not because they *have* to, like the lion, the leopard and the snake, but because they *can*. A part of me believed almost cynically that the mistrust of humans had become part of the genetic memory of every living species. The snake was sussing me out. It stopped again and this time it raised its head above the level of the rest of its body. Its eyes bulged as it looked at me, at the same time moving its head from side to side. It was doing this so that it could get an accurate perception of the depth and distance of my position. Had I moved, it would have picked up all the information that it needed about me, but I kept utterly still.

It was right next to me, when, for the first time, I slowly moved my stick towards it. Extending my right hand behind me, I opened the palm to signal to Jessie, whose footsteps I could hear coming up from below, not to proceed any closer. Meanwhile, I had no intention of harming the snake. I wanted to communicate to it that it was within the critical distance of my personal space. I was not comfortable. Either I was going to take action, or it would have to. It then nudged itself against the extended stick and I watched in awe as it curled itself around the lower end of the stick.

'What's happening up there?' Jessie had seen my hand telling her to stop. 'What's happening?' she whispered again.

'Shhh ... Take it very slow. There's a snake on the end of my stick,' I whispered back, taking my eyes off the creature for a split second.

'Really?' she whispered with enthusiasm, craning her head past my body to see what had captured my attention. But there was nothing to see, for when I had looked again, the snake had vanished.

Jessie gazed at the end of the stick and then at me.

'Were you being serious?' she asked me incredulously. Perhaps she thought that I had had a sudden onset of altitude sickness. Hallucination is a well-known symptom of this condition.

'Yes ... definitely ... it was there and suddenly it was gone ...' I stammered.

It occurred to me that healing was like that ... it comes after a face-to-face confrontation with something deep in oneself ... something intensely personal, something indescribable, unpredictable and rarely repeatable.

★   ★   ★

Now the serpent was more subtle than any of the beasts of the field ...

I remembered what Hugh had said about the oracle at Delphi: '*The oracle at Delphi does not speak clearly, but it does not mislead – its message is a subtle one.*'

'Thomas, how long is it before we get to Machame camp?' I asked.

'Maybe in half an hour,' he mumbled. The 'half-hour' turned out to be at least two hours. That, I discovered, was how Thomas operated. He would purposely underestimate the time and distance, lulling us into a sense of false cheer about our progress. Intrigued, but a little irritated by this, I asked him why he did it. If he had answered that he did it on purpose, that people sometimes needed a bit of confidence, even if it was false, then I would have been satisfied. But he shook his head and with a smile he said he was not sure why he did it. I wondered about that, because it typified a peculiar style among many African people. They will tell you what you *want* to hear, rather than what you may *need* to hear.

Brian had something to say about this. He said it could have been born out of a kind of traditional African respect for the person who was asking the question, not wanting to disappoint them, but without trying to mislead. This was the romantic view, he said, because at the end of the day we *all* wished for our circumstances to work out well, allowing for the unexpected.

'On the other hand,' he once said, 'it has become a kind of black man's burden, a disease, a hangover if you like, from the colonial policies. It is the "master–servant" *thing*. The black man gets the blame for *anything* that goes wrong. "Typical kaffir," they say. It's always the "kaffir's" fault and so, what do you expect? The servant, to protect himself, often gives misleading answers, which of course are interpreted as lies. This has to stop, you know. When we expect people to be stupid, they often act stupid. If we expect them to steal, then they will steal. I know this from my engineering company. If we expect people to be beggars, then they will beg. I'm not just referring to the black African,' he said. 'It's something to which all of us are prone. Think of our schooldays, Hamish … how many of us performed badly because we had already been labelled? And then there were those of us who were fortunate enough to have someone who *believed* in us … and we blossomed. The sooner we realise that we are *all* servants and masters, the better I believe our country is going to be. Otherwise we are going to perpetuate a consciousness of victims, one group blaming the other, the "when-we's" and the "you-owe-me's".'

How much longer? How much farther? 'These are typical first-world questions,' said Hugh, referring to our sometimes obsessive need to control our world.

'We've become a civilisation of control freaks,' he said, 'trying to manipulate every goddamn thing, including time, place and distance. God help us if we lose control. God help us if our predictions are wrong. God help us if we get lost!' he once said.

'I remember times in some of the wild places in Botswana where I was genuinely lost. I *had* to abandon my first-world concepts of time and distance. Sometimes I needed to keep moving. Sometimes I needed to stay put! Sometimes I had to let the wilderness *happen.* That can be scary.' I believed him.

19

... AND IN THE day that thou eatest of the fruit of the tree of knowledge of good and evil, thou shalt surely die.

Ye shall not surely die ... says the serpent. You shall live!

And they did eat of the fruit ... and their eyes were both opened.

There is no one like a friend to give a different perspective on life. When I was about six or seven years of age, John Kilburn, the boy from the smallholding next to ours, came strolling across the rolling lawn that led down from our home to the tree-lined entrance of our property. His hands were in his pockets and I could see him kicking at loose sticks and stones on the ground as he made his way up toward our front door. It was to be a watershed in my life. He had come by on one of those days that my parents 'happened' to be out. They felt I was old enough to be left by myself. In any case, William Phiri was around if anything went wrong. Their timing was uncanny.

It was an unintentional plot, or it was a big mistake on their part!

Up until then my life could only be described as blissful. Memories prior to that day were intermittent and vague. I could remember no prior significant cognitive or emotional events in my life. *I was naked and unashamed.* To put it another way, I was naïve.

Unknown to me at the time, a grave loss of innocence was at hand. Although I saw him coming, I was nevertheless startled by the loud knocking at the door.

Killy, as I would later call him, was four years older than me.

'Open up! I know you're there!'

It was as if he knew I was alone. I could not have imagined him shouting like that, had my parents been there.

'What do you want?' I asked. The squeak in my voice communicated my anxiety. What was I to do? My mother had cautioned me about him. I was afraid. I had this incredible sense of impending doom.

'I want to ask you something,' he said, sounding more and more like a lion trying to coax a warthog out of its den.

I now know who that visitor was. He was the incarnation of the serpent, Prometheus and Eve, all wrapped up in one. *They* had come to ask me a few questions. What could I do?

I let *them* in.

He pulled two cigarettes from his pocket and offered me one. I said no. It was a bad thing to do, I said. Killy laughed.

'Do you really believe all that stuff your mother told you – that if you played with it, it would fall off; that if you smoked, you would end up a dwarf? Do you still believe in Father Christmas?'

My eyes were wide in a combination of fear and astonishment.

'It's all bullshit,' he said.

I was confused and he knew it. He needled me again, 'Come on!' He challenged me.

'Just one puff?'

For me, on that fateful day, there was no turning back.

What my Promethean neighbour was really saying to me, was this:

'Wake up! Live!'

When my parents came back home, the look in their eyes said everything – *Where art thou?*

They knew something had happened to me. I was not at 'home'.

The more I thought about it, the more I came to sense in the synchronicity of my awakening a kind of archetypal plot, a pattern of Genesis that repeats itself generation after generation.

Our parents cannot protect us from the sweet influences of Prometheus, the serpent or the likes of John Kilburn. They have to leave us on our own some time, the way that they too were left alone. And they know what will happen – the fruit will be eaten, the fire will be stolen, Kilburn will come visiting.

We are all artists. We are all god-makers and explorers. We have to wait until the fathers and mothers are out of the 'garden', before we can taste the fruit of consciousness. Surely, the gods know that.

Which one of us, as a child, has not scrounged through our mother's and father's drawers and cupboards while they were out of the house? What were we looking for? Were we not trying to find out a little more about our creators, our mothers and fathers? Were we not trying to find out a little more about ourselves? After all, we were made in their image. Who were these 'gods'? And who were *we*?

It did not take long to find out some of their secrets. We found them in their cupboards, in the love letters, the French letters, the loaded gun, the wooden leg in the basement – so that's why Grandma limped – the wedding ring with the strange initials, the birth certificate with someone else's name on it, the faded photograph in that old suitcase in the attic, and the pills which said *'Keep away from children'*.

In a way we found what we were looking for. We were given our first hint of the fallibility of our gods. We were uncovering their dark side.

'This didn't mean that they were evil,' Jessie responded, when we spoke about all of this. 'No! To have a dark side is to be human. Since when had darkness become confused with evil?' she asked rhetorically. 'God knows how Africa has suffered as a result of that misconception.'

'To be catapulted into new levels of consciousness, costs us. It is painful,' she added.

'We lose something that we can never get back – our garden *innocence*. It is written all over our faces. It is in our eyes. It is in our body language. Our relationship with our gods will have changed forever.'

And the eyes of them both were opened.

And when God returned ... in the cool of the day, Adam and his wife hid themselves. And God called unto Adam and said, 'Where art thou?'

Things in Eden would never be the same again.

★   ★   ★

John Kilburn was my friend. It was a soul thing. How could I forget him? I would have gone to war with him. A restless searcher, he died when he was in his forties. As sometimes happens with artists, his soul could not keep up with his spirit.

20

IT WAS SUNDAY afternoon, exactly five twenty-two. We had arrived at Machame campsite on the upper edge of Kilimanjaro's rainforest, three thousand metres above sea level. The forest ended suddenly. It was hard to believe that humans had not had a hand in that abrupt demarcation between the forest and the higher moorlands. We usually put everything into squares and straight lines or we leave a mess.

The porters had pitched our tents just inside the edge of the forest.

'This is where we're going to sleep tonight,' I said to Jessie. 'On a geographical cross-over.'

'Is that not how it usually is when we go to sleep?' she responded, referring to the cross-over state of consciousness.

From the ridge and looking eastwards, I had a clear view of Kilimanjaro. It was partly covered with cloud and once again it struck me that it was not a mountain that would give easily of itself. I would have to wait until it was ready for me.

Lucas Steyn's group had already set up camp above the ridge. They looked relaxed, chatting away to each other. One of their porters was going from one member to another, pouring tea from a blackened kettle.

Lucas Steyn was sussing me out. I could see him looking me up and down. Even though the temperature had dropped to around ten degrees Celsius and the rest of the party had donned jerseys and head-warmers, he was still wearing his faded khaki shirt with its short sleeves rolled up an extra turn or two, exposing powerful biceps.

'What kept you guys?' he asked me, with a slightly mocking tone. 'We've been here for two hours already!'

I felt a twinge of irritation, but a part of me was expecting it.

'It's beautiful up here, isn't it?' I remarked, changing the subject and turning my eyes to the terrain beyond the ridge. He smiled as I walked past him and upwards to where the porters had lit a fire. Around the crackling flames they had erected a circle of sticks onto which they had placed an assortment of wet footwear, to dry out. It was an amusing sight of suspended, open-mouthed shoes and boots, looking like a choir of complaining faces. I took a photograph of it.

The sun came out from below the cloud line, lighting up the smoke-filled gaps between the trees. Something made me look behind and as I turned, Kilimanjaro showed herself. Her western face was a blush of pink and red, sharply contrasting against her pale glacial fingers. Behind her the sky was steel-blue.

The light was softening rapidly and I had to reduce the shutter speed on the camera to get as clear an image as possible on film. The slower the shutter speed, the greater the likelihood of blurring the image. Not having my tripod with me, I manually steadied the camera as best I could. Whatever the result, I knew that a photograph would not be able to capture what I had just experienced.

One of Lucas Steyn's group sidled up to where I was standing and greeted me. He was standing on lower ground than me, which meant that I had to look down at him. This made me feel uncomfortable and I moved down to his level. He looked down at my boots and asked me if they had been okay. I saw that he was wearing the same brand as mine and I told him about my blister. He said he was not sure about his boots. He had been worried, because he had only bought them a couple of days before coming to Tanzania. 'I might have a couple of blisters,' he said.

It was all small talk and I wondered what he was really wanting to say.

'By the way, my name is Hamish Malcolm,' I said, formally introducing myself.

'I'm David ... David Joseph,' he said and we shook hands.

'You're a doctor, aren't you?' he asked.

Here it comes, I thought – the hidden agenda.

'That's right.' My thoughts shifted into medical mode. I knew his question was not merely one of curiosity. I could see that he was pale, but I didn't jump to any conclusions.

'You guys got up here pretty early,' I ventured.

He nodded without saying anything and then he looked back to where the rest of his group was standing, as if making sure that no one would hear what he was going to say to me.

'We came up far too fucking fast,' he said.

His outburst took me by surprise. He must have seen my raised eyebrows.

'Excuse the language,' he said apologetically, 'but I'm a bit pissed off. I really took strain today.'

'Are you okay?'

'I've got a splitting headache,' he said, rubbing his right temple. 'I've taken something for it. It should be okay soon.'

'We didn't have to go so damn fast,' he continued. 'We arrived here about two and a half hours ago. We broke the bloody land speed record, thanks to Camel Man!'

I let him get what he had to say off his chest. 'It was so beautiful in the rainforest, but I hardly had a chance to enjoy it. That guy is crazy,' he said nudging his head in the direction of Steyn. 'He pushed us the whole way. Come on! Come on! Come on!'

I felt sorry for him. I also felt anger toward Lucas Steyn.

'Didn't they tell you to take it easy ... *pol-e, pol-e*?'

'Yes, but he told us it wasn't that important to go slowly on the first day. He'd done mountains like this before, he boasted. Pushing ourselves was supposed to be part of the challenge.'

'That's a pity,' I said. 'As far as I understand, you have to go easy all the time – unless you've grown up in high altitudes. It's a part of the acclimatising process.

Did you know any of the people you're with, before the climb?' I was trying to find out how he had got involved with Steyn.

'No, I was a late replacement for a friend who couldn't make it,' he answered.

'What do you know about Tarzan?' I asked, referring to Lucas Steyn.

David Joseph smiled at the image. 'Apparently he's a professional hunter and scuba diver and does those kinds of trips as well. This is his *first* trip to Kilimanjaro.'

'I thought so.' I thought back to the aircraft and the mountain through the window.

'He said his father had climbed Kilimanjaro back in the fifties … in record time … according to him. He said it took them less than three days to the top.'

'You can see what he's up to, can't you?' I asked.

'Trying to outdo his father!'

'Maybe,' I replied. 'Listen … if you want to, you can always join our party.'

David Joseph scratched his head beneath his cap.

'Thanks, Hamish … thanks. That's good to know.'

I sensed that Jessie may have been wondering where I was. I had told her that I was coming up to the ridge to take a few shots while the light was good, but the sun was already below the horizon.

'Let me know if I can be of any help tonight, otherwise, if it's okay with you, I'll check you out in the morning,' I offered.

'Thanks a lot and good luck … it was nice to meet you.'

It had become decidedly colder. Lucas Steyn was still in his shirtsleeves. He was pointing toward the glaciers, trying to describe something to someone who was looking through binoculars.

The light on the rock faces of Kibo Peak had turned to pale blues and greys. The moon, in its late waxing phase, loomed high over the ridge of Kilimanjaro's sleeping crater. It would be full moon in three nights' time, the night of our final ascent.

★   ★   ★

I had to get it off my chest and I told Jessie what had happened. 'He's not a bloody racehorse,' I said, referring to David Joseph while looking back up toward the ridge. 'We haven't come here to become other people's champions or to perform for anyone but ourselves.' I was angry. Jessie lifted my arm and placed it over her shoulder. 'I'm treating this climb like a lap of honour,' she said.

★   ★   ★

Thomas and his assistants had pitched their tents not too far from ours. They had also got the fire going. Our tent had a low, short tunnel at the entrance, making it look like an igloo. My knees had already stiffened from the day's climb and I wasn't looking forward to getting in and out of that tent.

Camping just below the ridge meant that our tents were sheltered from the open sky. This would protect us from the dew and if the temperature dropped to freezing, which was likely, we would escape the frost.

Jessie had put on a fleece-lined tracksuit, warm socks and cross-trainer shoes. Her boots were at the fireside. They looked exhausted lying on their sides, drying out like that.

Julius had made tea, which was very welcome. It was hot and sweet.

Brian was standing at the fire. His arms were folded and he was peering into the flames. He declined the tea, but agreed to have some soup instead. Jessie was most concerned about him not eating or drinking.

It was dark by the time supper was placed on the floral plastic tablecloth that Julius had spread onto the ground. We were served thin soup, bread, spaghetti, cabbage, cheese, jam and fruit. I had a little of everything, but Brian could only handle a few mouthfuls of soup before he got up and headed into the shadows. We heard

105

him vomiting and Hugh and I got up from the ground and went to be with him. Thomas waited at the fire.

Brian was leaning over with his hands on his knees.

'If I feel like this now, then I haven't got a whisper of a prayer of making it any further,' he said, spitting, and then wiping his mouth with the back of his gloved hand.

'I think you should go to bed. Come!' I led him away by one arm while Hugh held him by the other. Thomas had moved down to the tent which Brian and Hugh were going to share and stood at the entrance.

'Let's see how you feel in the morning,' I suggested. 'I'll bring you some drinking water and some Diamox. I think you must try and keep your fluid levels up. It will help.'

'Maybe in the morning you will be stronger,' Thomas reassured him.

Returning to the fire, I suddenly felt weary. I asked Jessie if she was ready for bed and she sighed, 'I thought you were never going to ask.'

★   ★   ★

And the evening and the morning were the first day. And it was good.

★   ★   ★

Hugh had suggested that Jessie and I should zip our sleeping-bags together to get as much body warmth as possible. It certainly was cold enough to share our body heat, but we talked ourselves out of it. The effort of having to get the bags together and then trying to get the zipper to work didn't seem worth it.

Eventually, tucked into my sleeping-bag, I turned to say goodnight to Jessie but she said, 'Wait a second. Listen to this.' Using a headlamp, she read to me what the Kilimanjaro guide map said about day one:

First. Don't underestimate the mountain. Kilimanjaro is BIG and the whole exercise is HARD WORK!

Park gate to 3000m – The first hour or so's walk is a novel experience. The scenery is interesting and if you left early, it is still quite cool. Pulse rate is between 100–120 and the breathing rate is about one cycle for every 3–4 steps. By 11 a.m. it has started to warm up, so you are sweating a bit. The legs start to feel the strain of non-stop up-hill walking and the calf muscles ache. A sit-down breather every 30–40 minutes is welcome. After you reach the first camp, a cup of tea/coffee revives you rapidly, and within an hour you feel almost normal.

I closed my eyes and thought about Brian, the forest, the mountain and the cold. For the first time I began to wonder … *What the hell am I doing here?*

Jessie said that clients often wondered 'what the hell' they were doing with their lives. It sometimes came as a gentle self-questioning. Sometimes it was urgent. Answering that question was hard work.

★   ★   ★

A snake slithered its way into my drowsy thoughts, pulling me back from the edge of sleep. I could see it wrapping itself around the end of the walking-stick. It became the snake that wrapped itself around the staff of Aesclepius, the god of healing. Then it became the serpent wrapped around the tree of the knowledge of good and evil. Were they not the same thing? Then, like the double helix of DNA, they became two, wrapping themselves around the staff of Hermes, that mercurial messenger of the gods. Hermes was also the god of medicines and of thieves. Were he, the serpent of Eden, and Prometheus, that thief of fire, about the same business?

I began to see the snake as being central to the process of healing and therefore one of its most profound symbols. By virtue of its repeated ability to outgrow its skin, what other creature better symbolised the human capacity to grow, to mature, to become more aware, to be healed. After more than two thousand years, the Aesclepian serpent is still the symbol of healing.

'The forbidden fruit is the fire of the gods,' said Jessie. 'It is the fire of consciousness. Without it, we can not know ourselves. With it, we can begin to give Eden's God a human face.'

'But it costs us,' she added. 'It's not for free and it's not all fun. *Knowing* the pain and sorrow of the human condition is part of the price. As far as I'm aware, we are the only creatures who know we are going to die. That's a huge torment for some people. Consciousness means *knowing* that we will be abandoned, but we will also abandon, that we will be betrayed and we will betray. *Knowing* this helps us to live with our wounds … we can't make our pain go away. But more than this, Hamish, I believe consciousness brings with it the capacity to forgive.'

★   ★   ★

I woke up several times during the night, my shoulders and hips aching from the pressure of my body on the thin mattress. I lost count of how many times I had to keep shifting position before I could fall asleep again.

Shortly before dawn, I had a dream that I was climbing a mountain somewhere in Africa. Looking down, I could see a tree-lined valley and a full winding river that flowed through it. I could see it all from a high ridge on the mountainside. The scene changed. I was in a boat on the river. I was a boy and I was fishing. Something powerful pulled on the end of my line and my rod bent heavily under the strain of whatever it was that I had hooked. I was reeling it in and as it neared the surface I could see that it was a large silvery fish. As it broke the surface of the water, its fin turned into a hairy arm, while the rest of its body began to take on the shape of a primate, not unlike a chimpanzee. Reaching down to pull it up out of the water, I grabbed it by the shoulder and in doing so, the hairiness disappeared. Suddenly, I found myself looking into a human face. I was both startled and afraid, watching it twist and turn as it fought to go back. I let it go and as I watched it becoming once more an ape and then a silvery fish, I felt a great sadness. I wanted to go with it. Something was holding me back. Looking behind me, I saw the path leading up the mountain and on the path, a snake. It had been watching me. Then it was gone.

I awoke and my shoulders and ribs ached.

It was first light. Something was different about the dawn. I listened for sounds of the day and then I realised what it was.

It was the silence. There were no birdcalls ... no francolins, no sparrows or robins here. Then I realised how high we were.

It was also cold. I turned to see if Jessie was awake and she looked at me through her eyelashes. She smiled, making a soft 'mmm' sound, which I interpreted as 'good morning'. I stroked the smiling wrinkle with the back of my hand and she closed her eyes again. Turning onto my back I thought about the dream. I thought about the snake that wrapped itself around my stick in the rainforest and then I wondered, *who had been dreaming whom?*

The evolutionary thread of the dream was unmistakable, as if it was saying, 'Don't forget where you've come from.' I could live with that. I had no problems with the concept of evolutionary beginnings and evolutionary processes. I was beginning to see evolution as more than a theory of origins. It was a phenomenon that occurred within the life span of every individual, a process of transformation on many levels – individual and social. There were physical changes from the embryo through childhood to adulthood and old age; cognitive changes from concrete to symbolic and abstract thinking; spiritual changes from god-fearing to god-making.

It was the face of the boy in the dream that disturbed me, however. It was the face of a young boy, ten or eleven years old. It could only have been me. He wanted to go back to the deep, but he couldn't. Instead, there was a winding path that beckoned. And the snake was watching.

★   ★   ★

I was ten years old when I was sent from my home in the bush, to boarding-school in Cape Town. I was out of Eden. I wanted to go back. I wanted to die.

Six years later, I left another Eden behind me. It was on that winter day when I looked into my father's eyes and I knew ... he was going to die. Something in me died, also.

21

NATURE CALLED AND I awkwardly manoeuvred myself out of the little tent, trying not to disturb Jessie.

'While you're up, will you see if there's any coffee?' she asked.

I headed off to a newly erected long-drop toilet, just beyond the campsite.

It was Monday, six-thirty a.m. It was the morning of the second day.

Up on the ridge, rays from the morning sun inched their way like fingers around the high southern slopes of Kibo Peak. The wrinkled crevices on the western face were in shadow, rather like Jessie's face that morning. I greeted the mountain and then I asked its permission to take a photograph. I wanted to capture a very different mood from the previous evening.

Taking a photograph with the sun directly in front of you usually causes a pink, star-like lens reflection on the picture. Sometimes a polaroid filter helps to minimise the glare.

I heard the sound of backpacks being zipped up and I looked up to see that Lucas Steyn's team was preparing to leave. I could see by his body language that he was irritable. Every movement was a statement of urgency.

Watching all of this, I began to see a lighter side to Steyn's behaviour. His seriousness was unwittingly amusing and for the first time I felt myself smiling at him. I was glad I was not with him.

He then started barking orders, telling people where they had to position themselves in the climbing line. I wondered how far he was going to push his group that day. Then I saw David Joseph adjusting his daypack. Hands in pockets, I strolled up to him.

'You guys are leaving pretty early,' I said, greeting him.

David shook his head and said Steyn wanted to reach a particular campsite above the Shira plateau.

'Above the plateau?' I asked. I was surprised, then I was concerned. Lucas Steyn was going to push it again. The plateau was where we were going to do our acclimatising and he was going higher!

'Yeah, he's aiming for a place called Lava Rock.' I had never heard of it.

'You look a bit better this morning,' I ventured.

'Yes, I'm okay,' he said. 'But if he wants to burn up the trail like yesterday, I'm going to tell him to cool it.'

'Take it easy.' I patted him on his shoulder. 'Don't forget the offer to join us. Good luck!'

The ridge was alive with porters and climbers. I could see the Swiss party, with Helen and Carol, packing up to go. Julius waved at me.

Jessie joined me and we watched Steyn's group heading up and over the Machame ridge.

'Do you know how Brian is feeling this morning?' I asked.

She said he was feeling easier and that he was going to see how the day progressed.

'I'm worried about him, Jessie.'

'Me too … come, let's have some breakfast. It's cornflakes, scrambled egg and tea,' she said, taking my hand.

It was time to move on. Thomas said we would be at Shira by two or three o'clock that afternoon if we left at eight a.m. as planned. We were on time. The campsite was cleared of litter and we were ready to face the steep trek up to the Shira plateau. I was dressed differently from the day before, wearing tracksuit longs over my shorts, a long-sleeved shirt with a pullover loosely tied over my shoulders. I would soon be wearing it, for already there was grey cloud cover above us. The breeze had a few sharp teeth in it and with the sun hidden, I could feel the temperature dropping. The porters had gone ahead with the tents and camping equipment, leaving us to begin our slow amble along the upward path, out of the rainforest and into the moorland wilderness. Julius and Jessie were up front. Hugh was just in front of me in the middle of our group, while Brian and Thomas brought up the rear.

Between breaths I told Hugh about the snake thoughts.

'Do you know that there's a homeopathic remedy which uses diluted doses of snake venom?' he asked. 'It goes by the name of *lachesis*, which comes from classical mythology. It was the name of one of the Fates whose duty it was to determine the length of each individual's life. Anyway, *lachesis* is the serpentine remedy for people whose lives are one-sided – overly conforming and controlled.'

'That sounds like the forbidden fruit of Eden.'

'That's right,' said Hugh. 'When a person says, there's something in me that wants out, that person needs *lachesis*.'

'Then the forbidden fruit is the remedy for those who are afraid of the *death* and the *life* that goes with the winding way of the serpent?'

'Yes, and talking about the winding way of the serpent, who said being straight and being honest is the same thing?' asked Hugh.

'What do you mean?'

'Well, it's not in our nature to be straight. Nature is intrinsically honest and we can hardly call nature straight. Look at the elements – surely there's nothing more honest than fire and yet it twists as it burns. Water curves its way through life ... so does blood ... and they're honest.'

'And what about the double helix of our DNA, the very fibres of our being?' I asked. 'There's nothing straight about them.'

'We can hardly call those genetic strands dishonest,' he answered.

I looked up to see our path winding its way up into the cloud line.

'Do you know something, Hugh?' I added. 'I feel most honest when I say, *Ja ... Nee*, as the Afrikaners do ... two answers in one. Yes ... No. Maybe ... maybe not.'

★   ★   ★

I thought about the way modern medicine and psychiatry would interpret the complaint of a half-lived life, of having a sense that one's creativity had diminished, that the *fire* had gone out. We would probably diagnose the patient as having a chemical imbalance.

★   ★   ★

'For Adam, the consequences of having tasted the forbidden fruit were formidable. It included a fire-and-brimstone sermon from God,' Jessie said. *'Because thou hast hearkened unto the voice of thy wife* – a very negative image of the woman, don't you think? – *cursed is the ground for thy sake, in sorrow shalt thou eat of it all the days of thy life; thorns and thistles shall it bring forth to thee.* How would you like to be spoken to like that?'

'Adam's fate was well prescribed,' she added. 'It was a king-size guilt trip. He must have held his breath, but then he did something quite astonishing. He didn't try to extricate himself from the blame.'

She continued. 'He didn't blame his wife, or the serpent in the garden, as he had done before. Instead, he *named* his wife. He *called his wife's name Eve*. In the story, it was as if he became aware of his companion on a different level. Psychologically, it was a huge wake-up call for him. He acknowledged the bone of his bones, the flesh of his flesh. She was a part of him, for without her there would have been no awakening. Without her there would have been no consciousness. He named his soul.' The look in Jessie's eyes was one of mischief and delight.

'Adam had come of age ... he stopped blaming. In essence, what he was saying to his father was this – I would like your blessing, but I don't need your approval.' Maybe it has to be that way, in that order – we first have to quit blaming. Then we can take a look at ourselves, acknowledging what it is that uniquely *animates* us. Finally, approval becomes an internal thing.'

I liked that ... Adam refusing to be a victim. I thought about Brian's refusal to be a political victim.

113

'I wonder what you would have done if your father had spoken to you like that, spelling out your fate?' Jessie asked.

'I think I might have done what Adam did. A part of me would have told him to get stuffed.'

★　　　★　　　★

My pace was now in keeping with my breathing – one breath for every step. My eyes were focused on the path beneath my feet. For a while, I had the feeling that it was carrying me.

We were well over three thousand metres above sea level, about three hours into the day's climb. Around me the vegetation consisted mainly of heath and protea bushes, covered in thickly matted strands of algae. I was not surprised when Jessie told me that the algae on the vegetation was called 'grandfather's beard', which thrived in the perennial moistness of the region.

The climb was steep and winding. We stopped often, not so much to rest but to allow the porters from other parties to pass by. It impressed me how fit and strong these men were, some of them carrying huge packs on their heads. The altitude didn't seem to bother them at all. I saw one porter carrying a chemical toilet on his head. I wondered if it belonged to the Swiss party.

Looking back, I could see the thick green canopy of the rain-forest and beyond that, Mount Meru. Up ahead, the mist was alive. It had long curling fingers that reached silently down the upper slopes towards us. Through a gap in the mist I could see the outline of a ridge not too far away. I knew from experience it was not as close to us as it looked.

Mountains are like that. Just when you think you are nearing that final ridge, you discover that there are still another two or three ridges in between.

I figured that the task of *knowing thyself* was also like that.

Thomas saw me looking up at the ridge and told me that after we had crossed it, we would be on the Shira plateau. From there, he said, it was an easy walk to the camp.

I looked at him suspiciously and told him that the word 'easy' did not belong on Kilimanjaro. He chuckled and then looked away. Thomas looked relaxed and his body language was a lesson in patience. He had kept close to Brian all morning, gently urging him on. Brian still looked pale, but he seemed to be managing. There had been little talking between us that morning, but I think that we had all sensed a need for quietness. I also sensed that Brian did not want to be asked too often how he was feeling.

At the different resting points, we all encouraged him in our own way. Hugh would pat him on his shoulder. I gave him the thumbs-up sign. Jessie offered him fluids.

She and I were walking closely together.

'How're *you* doing?' I asked her.

'Fine thanks. And you?'

'Don't you think you answered that a little too quickly? Fine-thanks-and-you?'

'Actually, I was thinking about Brian,' she agreed. 'I think he's brave to press on like he's done. I was wondering what I would've done if I felt as ill as he'd been last night. I mean … what would you have done if I was too ill to carry on and I had to turn back?' she queried.

'I knew you were going to ask me that question. Do you really want to know?'

'Mmm-hmmm.'

'I would have stayed with you,' I assured her. 'And if it was me? What would you have done?' I had a feeling that I was walking into a trap.

'I would have gone on without you!'

'You answered that too quickly,' I said, not believing her, yet feeling a pang of hurt somewhere in my solar plexus.

'I'm not my husband's keeper,' she said, looking down her nose at me.

'I'll remember that,' I said, nodding my head slowly but giving her a look that said, 'Just you wait.'

★ ★ ★

Adam's action, ignoring the 'father' and quietly naming his soul, evoked an astonishing response from the Creator. He came to their help. He clothed them. He offered protection. He showed compassion. He showed a human face. Adam's transformation was also his.

And the eyes of them both were opened, and they knew that they were naked; and they sewed fig leaves together and made themselves aprons ...

Jessie saw in this two vulnerable egos each in need of a *persona* – the fig leaves and the skins – those masks that we present to the world, not because we want to, but because we *have* to. Our emerging egos and our ego skills are too fragile to be on full display, she said. They are unworldly and vulnerable. As an example, she referred to Joseph of Genesis as a 'daddy's boy', the round-faced dreamer, naïvely showing off his multicoloured world views, coming across as a tattletail and a 'know-all'.

'You can't do that,' she said. 'And you know what happened to him ... he was left for dead. The world does that to the Josephs of the world, Hamish ... they *crucify* them. However, Joseph survived his dark night of the soul,' she added. ... 'He kept his dreams alive.'

When the temperature changes we put on the appropriate clothing. The same with the ego, Jessie said. We put on different personas when the social climate changes. She called it a 'survival strategy'.

I thought about the necessity of having to wear those socially acceptable masks. We wear many ... the mask of modesty, the mask of the gentleman, the kind lady, the happy family, the pious father, the good boy, the innocent victim, the dutiful wife and so on. Sometimes, we get stuck in our personas. The more we identify with our masks, the more difficult they become to take off.

A few years back I came home from the hospital wearing my white coat. My stethoscope hung around my neck like a limp scarf. I walked into the lounge and my eldest daughter, who was seventeen years old, took one look at me. 'Are we part of your ward round, Dad?' she protested gently. I remembered feeling quite sheepish.

The doctor's white coat is another kind of persona or mask. It is a kind of 'fig leaf'. Its value goes beyond the supposed protection of the doctor's clothing from germs and so on. It is also a symbolic uniform, the cloak of the disciples of Aesclepius, those original shamans, schooled in the ancient secrets of medicines, cleanliness and healthy thought. It is also a kind of armour, protecting the vulnerability and the anxiety of the one who is wearing it. I know. I still have one. It needs to be taken off, from time to time.

★   ★   ★

When I went to boarding-school, I learned how to survive. Even though John Kilburn had cautioned me that I was in for a rough time, I learned the hard way. I arrived unprotected, my multi-coloured notions on full display. It did not take long before I was brought down. I was bullied into doing it *their* way. I soon found out what it was like to be an outsider.

Pulled on the one hand to get the hell out, to go back home, I was pulled on the other, by Killy, to hang in … to see it through. John Kilburn stood by me.

'Pissheads!' I called them, referring to the bullies.

Killy put his arm around me and laughed.

★   ★   ★

At midday we stopped at a large rocky outcrop for lunch. Thomas told us the steepest section of the climb was over. From where I was standing it looked like the path up ahead had levelled out. I couldn't see much further than that because the mist was so thick. Lunch consisted of a boiled egg, a bread roll, lettuce, a small packet of peanuts and an orange. It was good. I put my head back against a boulder and closed my eyes for a minute. I didn't know that a boulder could be so comfortable. I could have fallen asleep had it not been for a group of Italian climbers that appeared out of the mist below us. They were wearing brightly coloured down-jackets that made them look more enthusiastic than they actually were. Arriving at the level ground around us, one of the Italians plopped to the ground and sat there with his head between his knees. He was groaning to himself and when he was offered a sandwich by one of his colleagues, he waved him away. I hoped he would be okay.

I strolled over to where Jessie was sitting and asked her to shift her body so that I could lean into her, back to back. I wriggled myself into the contours of her shoulders and her neck and then I closed my eyes. I knew it would not be long before Thomas gave us the signal to move on. Feeling the warmth of her body through our clothing, I began to doze off. I felt safe.

'I think we must zip our sleeping-bags together tonight,' she said. 'It's going to be colder than last night.'

'I was thinking the same thing,' I mumbled.

I remembered what Jessie had said to me on the bus. I too had the feeling that I had known *her* for thousands of years.

22

AND ADAM KNEW *Eve his wife; and she conceived and bare Cain ... and she again bare his brother Abel. And Abel was a keeper of sheep, but Cain was a tiller of the ground.*

One day the two of them brought their offerings to the father and in an unprecedented account of favouritism ... *the Lord had respect unto Abel and his offerings; but unto Cain and his offerings, he had no respect.*

What was going on? What kind of a father was this? What a bummer!

Cain was deeply wounded ... *he was very wroth and his countenance fell.*

Cain must have ached. He must have asked the question that so many of us ask – why me? Is there nothing in me that is acceptable? Is there no place where I fit?

How many of us know the rejected Cain in ourselves, I wondered?

What could he do? He could not challenge the father directly. How could he? He did not have the cognitive, emotional or physical equipment for that kind of confrontation. What he did, however, in a chilling act of displaced aggression, was to destroy the very thing that the father loved most. He killed his brother.

I know about displaced aggression. I think we all do. How many of us have unconsciously taken out our anger at someone else, on those who are close to us, sometimes younger or less able to defend themselves?

Why did this father so brazenly offend his older, 'streetwise' son, the tiller of the lands, the one who had to know the seasons, when to plant, when to prune? Why the one who had his ear to the ground and not the young and innocent keeper of the sheep?

Was it possible that Cain was too much like his father? Was it possible that not even God could see his own *blind spot*? He knew of Cain's capacity for rage and envy, but he could not recognise it in himself. Did he want his son to remain in the garden, to be more like Abel, more sheep-like? It seems that he didn't want an angry, street-wise thinker on his hands.

Was it possible that an unconscious father had failed to recognise his own shadow in his child?

What could be understood from all this? Perhaps it was this − that the most powerful influences in a young person's life come not from the formal teachings and consciousness of the parents, but from their parents' *unlived* lives, their dark and unaccepted sides. The child then, some more than others, embodies the *shadow* of the parent, so that they, the children, have to go out and find that church in the East that the parents have forgotten.

'Sometimes, as parents, we need our children in order that we may become more conscious of ourselves,' Jessie said.

Jessie often spoke about the child in the adult. In therapy, she said, the child is always there. In fact, it is likely that there is only one kind of therapy − child therapy. In a way, it is always the inner child that is being addressed. She spoke of the wounded child as an archetype, an evolutionary instinct of the psyche. Childhood wounds were inescapable, she had said, believing that the wounds of childhood were in the long term transforming. They were therefore strangely necessary.

'When you know this,' said Jessie, 'then a number of things become possible − unbearable memories become bearable, scars soften − they don't go away − but with time, *forgiveness* becomes a possibility.'

★   ★   ★

120

Brian looked less pale than he had been the day before and when he asked Hugh for a smoke, I knew that he must have been feeling better. He lit up and Jessie asked him for a puff. Like a naughty schoolgirl, she looked to see if I was watching.

'Just one puff,' she pleaded, looking at me.

'I am not my wife's keeper,' I responded playfully.

She held the cigarette between the tip of her thumb and forefinger, as if she was about to throw a dart. Her other three fingers fanned out to full extension, and with her eyes closed and her lips pursed, she took the deep breath of a learner smoker. I took a photograph of her hanging onto the end of the cigarette and the 'click' of the shutter precipitated a bout of red-faced coughing.

'Does your mother know that you smoke?' I queried, looking down my nose at her in my best headmaster pose.

★   ★   ★

Am I my brother's keeper?

'Five words in a stunning question,' said Jessie. 'Am I my brother's keeper?'

In her practice, Jessie did not know of a single man, woman or child who at some time in their lives had not harboured death fantasies about older or younger siblings, about their parents or spouses. Sometimes our deepest fears and our secret longings turned out to be the *same thing*, she said, and sometimes, they *happened* ... a younger sister died, an older brother became ill, a father left home and never came back, a mother took an overdose. Am I my brother's keeper? Am I in some way culpable?

'You remember Oedipus, don't you ... the central figure of Freud's so-called Oedipus complex?' she asked.

'Uh huh,' I nodded.

'When he discovered that he had unwittingly killed his father and then married his mother, he ordered that he should have his eyes put out. The people begged him not to punish himself like that. After all, how was he to know? *I should have known* was his answer. An amazing response,' she said. 'He blamed himself for his tragic loss of insight … blinding himself so that he could rediscover it.'

Am I my brother's keeper? I wondered who was tough enough or conscious enough to answer a question like that. I considered the seemingly impersonal tragedies that most of us would see as events beyond our control – an oil slick off the coast of Bavaria killing six thousand penguins. Five mountain gorillas dying in transit to a zoo. One million Hutus and two million Tutsis in an African genocide. Six million Jews … thirty-two school children … two million hectares of rainforest … gone … *Am I my brother's keeper?*

★   ★   ★

As rapidly and mysteriously as the mist had descended, so it began to lift. I could see a plateau stretching into the western distance ahead of me. It was a vast tract of land bordered in the south by the rugged granite pinnacles of Shira 'cathedral' and in the east by the massive sloping neck of Kilimanjaro. It was hard to believe that all of this land was part of one free-standing mountain. To the north, the plateau eased its way down into another country – Kenya.

From the western edge of the plateau, it was said you could see into the Great Rift Valley. As I began to picture it, I thought of the ancient scar of Africa and the place where water had poetically fallen away from itself. I remembered my father and then I felt something tracing its way down the front of my body. It was as if he was with me. Then came the powerful image of William Phiri. He was there, too.

In the near distance, I could see the welcome sight of dome-shaped tents. It was Shira camp. It was a good feeling to know that we had arrived at a place that had been prepared for us. I checked my watch and saw that it was two-thirty. It seemed a lot later than that.

From a fire that had been lit near an outcrop of rocks beyond the tents, a thin blue column of smoke threaded its curving course into a windless sky.

★   ★   ★

Arriving at the campsite, I counted at least a dozen tents in three different areas. I recognised those belonging to the Swiss group and the others, I figured, belonged to the Italians, who were still somewhere behind us on the trail. There was no sign of Lucas Steyn. They must have pushed ahead, I thought.

I wondered how David Joseph was.

At the campsite, Julius brought us tea and popcorn that had been prepared on the fire at the porters' site. It tasted good, but I quickly realised that I was not as hungry as I thought I was. Jessie asked Thomas if he had children and he said he had a son and two daughters. His son was sixteen years old.

'Is he also going to be a guide?' asked Hugh.

Thomas pulled on his bottom lip and shook his head. 'I will *never* bring him to this mountain.'

'Why not?' Jessie asked in surprise. 'This mountain is so special.' Thomas shook his head again. 'That is why I do not want to bring him here. If I bring him to this place, I know what will happen. He will want to stop going to school.'

The porters had gathered around a large open fire. It was situated below and within a hollow granite outcrop, not quite a cave, but deep enough to provide reasonable shelter if it rained.

I remembered my father telling me that he and William had taken shelter in a rocky overhang during one of their nights on the mountain. I had a strong feeling that it must have been the one that I was looking at.

Two alpine chats were hopping around close to our tents. They looked very similar to the *Cercomela familiaris*, or familiar chat, back home. Because of the cold, their feathers were all fluffed up, making them look round and plump. They cocked their heads from side to side, keeping a constant eye on the bowl of popcorn. The female chat eventually plucked up the courage to perch on the rim of the bowl and after a brief look around her she jumped in. I knew what it was like to be on the edge of the unknown and then jump in.

There was still ample daylight to get ourselves organised, but Jessie had already zipped our sleeping-bags together and had arranged our belongings in the tent so that the less essential things were out of the way. She said she had a slight headache and was going to lie down for a while. The down sleeping-bags looked very inviting and I lay down next to her. Turning onto my back, I focused on the pale-blue canopy of the tent and thought about our children and my mother. I could hear the blood pounding through my ears.

'Are you okay, sweetheart?' I asked. There was no answer.

Closing my eyes, I thought about Cain's grief. I felt for the man. I then realised that I was feeling for something deep in me.

23

THERE WAS A movement against my body, a nudge that reached from one world into another, from a world in which boundaries were clear into a world which I was not ready to let go of yet. The world I was in was a strangely attractive one of crossings, where feelings, thoughts and perceptions blurred into each other. I tucked my head deeper into the warmth of the sleeping-bag, hoping that the bright world of boundaries would go away. I was not ready to participate in that world just yet.

'Are you awake?' It was Jessie.

'No,' I answered.

'D'you know what time it is?'

'Mmm … mm.'

'We've been asleep for an hour and a half!'

I opened my eyes, and looking across the profile of Jessie's shoulders at the side of the tent, I slowly orientated myself to time and place.

'I must've slept with the dead,' she said. 'I don't think I moved.'

'I wrestled with Cain,' I moaned.

'You obviously didn't sleep much.'

Outside, the porters were talking away at the top of their voices. It sounded like some of them were trying to out-shout the others.

'I think they're making bets among themselves,' I mumbled, still unwilling to move from my sleeping-bag.

'What kind of bets?' asked Jessie.

'About *who* they think is going to make it to the top.'

It seemed to me that every journey had at least one turning point. The feeling in my stomach said that Shira plateau was going to be one of them.

★   ★   ★

I could feel it was decidedly colder than when I had crawled into the tent earlier, so I dressed myself in my denim jeans, polar-neck shirt and a gortex wind jacket.

Emerging from the tent, I literally creaked myself into the standing position and there, directly in front of me, I saw the sun leaning into the late afternoon. Behind me I witnessed an ancient game of hide-and-seek. Thick veils of mist had moved across the grand western face of Kilimanjaro, hiding Kibo peak. One of her high northern glaciers peeped through the cloud momentarily and when I looked again, it had gone. Suddenly, the southern ridge of the crater showed itself. The mountain was playing hide-and-seek again. I studied the ridge through my binoculars, trying to trace out a possible ascent route.

'Amazing, isn't it?' Hugh was standing beside me. He, too, was looking up at the mountain, his camera in his hand. I hadn't heard him coming up beside me.

'Yes, it is,' I said. 'I keep getting the feeling that this mountain is trying to say something to us.'

'Me too.'

We both stood there in silence, watching the colossus slowly unveil itself.

'Maybe it's reminding us that we hardly know her and that maybe we should ask her permission to be here,' said Hugh.

The show was not over. Like the opening of a curtain, the clouds peeled off into the wings of the granite amphitheatre, revealing the full western face of the mountain. She looked brilliant in the late-afternoon light. And there, above the northern shoulder of the massif, was the moon … a daughter in a timeless dance around her mother.

Kilimanjaro had shown herself again.

The sound of a rushing wind passed by overhead and looking up, I saw a large raptor gliding gracefully over the campsite. Hugh immediately recognised it as a bearded vulture, the lammergeyer, *Gypaetus barbatus*. I saw its head turn toward us and then with utter indifference, it looked away. I watched it until it became a little dot in the distance and then it was gone. I thought of the marabou stalks at Moshi and how, the vulture too, when in flight, was gracious in a way that other more handsome birds could never be.

I knew one or two people like that.

Looking back at the mountain I asked Hugh if he could remember the terror and the thrill of hide-and-seek. We laughed as we re-experienced the emotions.

'Is this not the only game that we play … Prey and predator?' he asked.

I agreed. Called by whatever name we wished, the games we played on those outer landscapes of the streets, the arenas, the rings, the ovals, as well as on the inner ones of dreams and fantasies, were all patterned, it seemed, with the excitement and the terror of hide-and-seek.

I remembered the terror of being hunted, of being warned. 'I'm coming to get you,' I also remembered the fear that perhaps I would never be found, that the game would go on without me. I remembered once shouting out, 'Here I am!'

I too was the hunter. I learned how to stalk, to listen, to choose my targets. I also knew the frustration of not finding what I was looking for. I learned a long time ago what it must have been like to be a lion, a zebra, a hyena, a cat or a mouse. I thought about the secret connection between the predator and the prey.

I wondered if in some way there was a connection between me and the mountain.

Who was hiding and who was doing the seeking?

★   ★   ★

The artist knows what it means to play hide-and-seek. He knows that the prey and the predator are linked, that the one becomes the other. Hide-and-seek, I think, is about searching for that which is searching for you.

★   ★   ★

It was nearly zero degrees Celsius. To warm us up, Julius had prepared a fire close to our tents. The sun had already set and the supper plates had been cleared. We had eaten thin soup again, bread, macaroni and cabbage. For dessert we had chocolate-flavoured pudding. It was like glue.

In the distance, way below the rainforest, I could once more see scattered fires glowing in the dark. There were people out there. I wondered if they could see our fire.

I love fires. It is as if the flames have a hypnotic power, drawing me to its core, making me look into it and beyond it, to the sun, to where the flames came from. There are hundreds of ancestors in a fire, all kinds of profiles, golden eyes that look back at you and then look away; all kinds of stories.

Looking around, I saw the flame-lit faces of Hugh, Brian and Jessie peering into the glow. I had an image of the lighting of the first human fires. I wondered if the great volcano on which we were standing could remember that day. I wondered if it had a memory of those primal human faces, reflecting in the glow of those first fires of Genesis. I thought of how those earliest fires got started, born out of *friction*, one object rubbing against another, this way, that way, chafing, peeling, wounding, heating, smoking, blowing, igniting, fire … Light!

I imagined a similar pattern of friction in the evolution of consciousness – friction – two ideas, two values, a thou-shalt and a thou-shalt-not, rubbing against each other, this way, that way, chafing, peeling, wounding, heating, igniting … Light!

If fire was the gift that allowed us to live in the dark, was consciousness a gift that allowed us to live *with* our darkness?

★   ★   ★

Jessie, her hands deep inside the pockets of her fleece-lined jacket, leaned into me and nudged me with her shoulder. It was her signal that it was bed-time.

Getting into our shared sleeping-bag, Jessie suddenly winced with pain. I saw that her left foot had curled up with cramp and, coming to her rescue, I stretched her toes into full extension. It helped. She had another two attacks before it eventually settled.

'Thanks for zipping the bags together, Jess. We're going to need some body warmth tonight,' I said.

Using my head lamp, I read aloud what the guide map said about day two: *3000m – 4000m. You will be a little stiff this morning but this wears off once you start walking. Pulse rate is between 100 – 120 per minute, and the breathing rate about one cycle for every three to four steps. A couple of blisters are forming, one on the instep and one on the small toe, but what the hell! Appetite still okay for tasty foods, but not too fatty. Leg cramps in the evening.* The author was spot-on.

It took a little while for the inside of the sleeping-bag to warm up. I was wearing socks, tracksuit longs and a T-shirt. Through my socks I could feel the plaster that I had put on for the developing blister. It hadn't bothered me at all during the day and I decided I would leave it alone, dressing and all. Lying on our sides, Jessie cuddled into me from behind. In that position, like two well-fitting teaspoons, we fell asleep.

★ ★ ★

It was dark outside. I didn't know what time it was, but something had woken me up. My heart was racing. I could not get enough air into my lungs. I sat up and looked to see if there was any ventilation in the tent, convinced that there was no air getting in. I reached over behind me to unzip the entrance cover. Jessie was awake.

'What's the matter, sweetie?'

'I can't breathe. There isn't enough air in here. This place hasn't got any ventilation.'

I gulped in the cold air that streamed into the tent from the unzipped opening, convincing myself that I was feeling easier, even though I was still short of breath.

It took a little while before I began to feel better, although I noticed I was breathing very deliberately. I wasn't used to concentrating on my breathing like that.

129

Jessie pointed to the two gauze openings at the top of the tent and said, 'Surely there's enough air coming through there?'

I then realised what was happening. Of course, there was more than enough air in the tent — it was just that while I had been sleeping, my breathing rate had slowed to below the optimal oxygen requirements for my brain. This then triggered the signals that woke me. I was in a dilemma. It was okay while I was awake, breathing voluntarily, but what would happen when I went back to sleep again?

I tried again, leaving a small opening at the tent entrance … just in case. Snuggling into Jessie's warmth again, I started to drift off, but I didn't get very far. The 'red lights' in the brain stem started flashing and once again I found myself sitting bolt upright, hungry for air and breathing deeply through my mouth.

'Are you okay?'

'It looks like the altitude is getting to me.' I tried not to convey the slight feeling of panic that had gripped my chest. I wished the morning would come.

I tried to go back to sleep again. This time, I placed my back-pack under my pillow to make sure that my head was higher than the rest of my body. I closed my eyes and focused on the rhythm of my breathing. The change in my head position seemed to have made a difference. Sleep started fingering its way into my thoughts and when I opened my eyes again it was light outside.

My eyes were all puffed up and when Jessie saw my face she had a little giggle.

'I wish you could see yourself.'

'I had a terrible night fighting off those intruders,' I groaned. 'Didn't you hear them?'

'What intruders?'

'The secret police!' I pointed to my eyes. 'It was them … they beat me up during the night.'

'That's what happens when you don't wash your face before going to bed,' she teased. The previous night I had refused to put cold water on my face.

I was relieved that the day had come and that I had been able to go back to sleep. But I was a little worried about what the following night would have in store for me.

'One thing about the mountain,' I said to Jessie, as I eased myself out of the sleeping-bag and pointed to my face, 'the higher you climb, the thinner your public persona becomes.'

24

'HAMISH! JESSIE!' IT was Hugh calling from outside of the tent. 'Are you awake?'

'Morning, Hugh. How is it out there?' I called.

'Come and check this!' he enthused.

It took a minute or two for us to pull on our jeans and boots before joining Hugh on the rocky outcrop outside our tent.

'Jesus … What happened to you?' he exclaimed, remarking on my puffy eyes. 'Did you sleep upside-down last night, or something?'

I told him about the secret police, which amused him, and then about my breathing, which concerned him.

'I just need a few more red blood cells and I should be okay,' I said, hoping that my body would respond to the low-oxygen altitude.

It was a crystal-clear morning with a pinch of the glaciers in the air. The sun was hiding behind the eastern face of Kilimanjaro, casting a shadow so huge that it stretched itself like a blanket across the lower half of Meru, spreading down over the full extent of the rainforest below. It was eerie in its massiveness.

Unlike her bigger, yet younger, sibling, Meru's volcanic fires had long since emptied themselves. She was a mellow older sister, the constant companion to her sleeping yet vibrant sister.

'It sometimes takes a long time to emerge from the shadow of the mothers, the fathers, the brothers and the sisters,' said Jessie, indicating toward the vast expanse of shade across Meru and the valleys below.

★ ★ ★

We were going to climb to 4 800 metres that day, returning once more before nightfall to Shira campsite. This was to give us an added day to acclimatise to the altitude. From 4 000 metres at Shira and upwards, the paucity of oxygen in the air became a powerful stimulus to the body to increase its oxygen-carrying capacity. This is a survival reflex of the body, activated and accomplished by a remarkably sensitive feedback mechanism involving the autonomic nervous system whereby neuro-chemical signals from the brain stimulate the bone marrow to produce more red blood cells. These are the cells that bind and carry molecules of oxygen to different parts of the body. The brain is more sensitive to oxygen-lack than any other organ. From the brain, electrical signals are relayed to the heart to beat faster, speeding up the circulation of the existing red blood cells. This process cannot be hurried unless you undergo a transfusion of compatible human red blood cells to bring up the cell volume. Athletes competing at high altitudes have been known to cheat in this way. However, it takes time to acclimatise. This is why climbers spend so much time at the 6 000-metre-high base camp of Mount Everest.

After what had happened to me during the night, I was pleased to have the extra day.

Our pace that morning was nice and slow. The early stages were not quite as steep as the previous morning and I could hear people chatting to each other without discomfort. The two Americans, Carol and Helen, had joined up with us for the day. They seemed to have less to say to each other. I think the mountain had something to do with that.

I thought about what Jessie had said – that it could take a long time to emerge from the shadows of our fathers and mothers. I wondered if those waves of anger I had experienced back home – the ones that I had associated with my father's death, and which now seemed to be lessening – had anything to do with a perception that I was beginning to emerge out of the shadow of my father. My thoughts then turned to my mother and I recalled Jessie telling me on the bus to Moshi that, when she first met me, I was a bit of a mommy's boy. I was still wrestling with that one. Maybe it was true. Maybe some of my anger had to do with being in her shadow. How often had I felt that I needed her approval? How often had I sometimes reluctantly taken my mother's advice for 'my own good'?

What kind of a hold do mothers have on us? I didn't realise that I was thinking aloud.

Hugh asked me what I was muttering about and I sheepishly told him that I was thinking about the influence of our mothers.

'Don't be too hard on them.' It was Jessie. 'We can't escape them, you know.'

'You were not supposed to be listening,' I teased.

★   ★   ★

Below me, Brian and Thomas were walking together. Brian was hanging in. He had not slept too well but he was going to see how things were at the end of the day.

Hugh plodded along in front of me, close enough for me to see the brand name on his climbing-boots. Up ahead was a cairn, a man-made pile of rocks, which stood like a sentinel next to the path. It was made up of a large boulder on which smaller rocks and stones of various shapes and sizes had been heaped. It had a human shape. There was a bright red smudge on one of the stones, as if someone had painted it on. When I got closer I could see that it was caused by red algae. As a species, algae are the great survivors of the world, adapting to all kinds of weather and terrain. They were around a long time before *Zinjanthropus*.

When I touched it, the cairn had a rough and flaky feel.

Like fires, cairns have a way of speaking to me. Maybe it is because there is something ancient about them – the signposts of our earliest explorations, the landmarks that showed the hunter the way home and to where they were headed.

It is said that whenever the nomadic Bushmen of the Kalahari went out in search of new hunting grounds, they built a cairn at the start of the new path that they were going to make. Each hunter, in turn, wet the palm of his hand with his tongue and then, placing the moistened skin on the uppermost stone on the cairn, called upon Nkulunkulu, the Great Spirit, asking that the path lead them to an eland or a springbok. The ritual had little to do with hoping that they would find what they were looking for. They *knew* what they were looking for. The path and the eland were *one*. I liked that. I licked the palm of my hand and placed it on top of the cairn and said a silent thank-you to those old Bushmen of Africa. They are gone now. The Bushmen no longer live as they did, not too long ago. Whenever I think of them, I think of the *Ziziphus* thorn that hooks backwards.

Hugh was still ahead of me. It was toward midday and by then I had spent so much time on the path looking down that I could tell with my eyes closed the colour of his laces, the contours around the edge of his boots as well as the patterns on his soles. His pace had been even and purposeful.

'Hey, Hugh!' I called. 'I hope we find what we are looking for.'

He stopped and turned around to look at me. And then, he smiled. He understood.

25

'JACOB WAS A mommy's boy … until he got to know Rachel,' said Jessie, referring to her favourite character in Genesis.

… and behold, there were twins in Rebekah's womb.

And the first came out red all over like an hairy garment; and they called his name Esau. And after that came his brother out, and his hand took hold on Esau's heel; and his name was Jacob.

And the boys grew: and Esau was a cunning hunter, a man of the field; and Jacob was a plain man, dwelling in tents.

And Isaac loved Esau, because he did eat of his venison: but Rebekah loved Jacob.

I could feel the tension in the verses. Something had to happen. Jacob's story could have been mine. Some of it could have been Hugh's.

'We all have a bit of Esau and Jacob in us,' said Jessie. 'Esau is our dark twin, the wild part of us. Jacob is the little boy that does what he is told, the refined and socially acceptable part, the part that our mothers like.'

I was drawn to Esau. I wanted to know his wildness. I began to see in him an uninhibited aspect of myself, primal but by no means primitive. His was not a wildness of the uncouth, but of something spontaneous and natural … something unprescribed, as Jessie had said. Like the Bushmen perhaps, he reminded me of something longed for and aboriginal in me.

'Esau comes alive when we say No! to the piles of rules and regulations of bureaucracies, when we say Enough! to the crippling anima of deconstructive academia … when we honour spontaneity and the glorious uncertainty of sport. Esau is that part of us that gets tired of *nice* talk. It's Esau that says, Cut the crap! He is necessary for our wholeness,' Jessie enthused.

'Jacob was something else,' she continued. 'Taking his mother's advice, he steals Esau's heritage. He knew it, and he was afraid … *I shall seem to him a deceiver; and I shall bring a curse upon me, and not a blessing*. But, listen to what his mother says … *Upon me be thy curse, my son: only obey my voice* … Don't worry, my boy, mommy is here.'

'Run, when you hear that!' Jessie said, raising her voice as she quoted from the fifteenth-century poet, Rumi.

'Which is what Jacob did,' she said, picking up on the story again, 'even if it was to escape his twin. He would have to confront him later.'

And Jacob ran *to Pa-dan-ar-am … and out from Beer-sheba and … to Haran.*

… he lighted upon a certain place, and tarried there all night, because the sun was set: and he took the stones of that place, and put them for his pillows, and lay down in that place to sleep.

'It is a wonderful image,' she said. 'For the first time in his life, Jacob was really alone … and in the wilderness too, not very comfortable either. In his sleep he dreams. He sees angels ascending and descending a ladder and then he hears a voice … *I am with thee, and will keep thee in all places whither thou goest and will bring thee again unto this land; for I will not leave thee until I have done that which I have spoken to thee of.* What a dream! What a voice! What do you think that was about?'

'Go on,' I said.

'It was the voice of that which was deepest and oldest in him. A calling of an ancient pattern of God, the pattern that connects us to our universe and to our fate.'

'I sense a hint of destiny in that, too,' I responded. 'In a way Jacob was speaking for himself.'

'Yes,' said Jessie. 'And his response to the dream was profound … *surely the Lord is in this place, and I knew it not* … It was as if, for the first time, he had touched something authentic in himself. He was in the process of leaving the garden.'

Jacob built a cairn and blessed it. It would stand as a pointer of his outward journey, his *Iliad*, as Hugh would have put it, but it was also the marker of his way back, his *Odyssey*. He still had to come back to confront Esau. And Jacob went on his way. He was on a journey to *somewhere*.

So were we.

26

THOMAS CALLED OUT that we should stop for a drink.

I could see the pulsing of the skin on my left wrist directly above the radial artery which is one of the major vessels supplying the hands with oxygenated blood. I felt my pulse: over a hundred beats a minute, forty beats more than my average resting pulse. I thought of my heart beating away, responding to different neuro-chemical messages from the brain. I thought of what lay ahead and then for the first time I felt a twinge of doubt about what I was trying to do.

★   ★   ★

Like the characters of Genesis, who in their own way endured personal rites of passage as they came to know themselves and the world differently, climbing the highest free-standing mountain in the world was becoming something of a rite of passage for me. I too was discovering certain parts of myself that I hadn't previously acknowledged ... doubt ... vulnerability ... resolve. It occurred to me that it was not so much the physical *leaving* of the mothers and fathers that was important, but rather, of coming to know them *differently* ... of enjoying their blessings perhaps, but no longer needing their approval.

I looked at Hugh resting not far from me. It seemed that most people who go through a divorce come to see the world differently.

★   ★   ★

Jessie looked lovely. Her cheeks, without make-up, were tinged with red. I passed the water bottle to her and watched her as she drank deeply. After an oatmeal biscuit and a drink, Thomas quietly urged us on.

★ ★ ★

… when Jacob saw Rachel, he went near and rolled the stone away from the well's mouth … and Jacob kissed Rachel.

'Love at first sight!' said Jessie.

'It's what happened to us,' I teased. Jessie blushed.

I remembered her describing falling in love, as a socially sanctioned psychosis. 'Think about it,' she said. 'We hear the voices of our lovers when they're not physically present. We lose our appetite and we lose sleep. For a while, we live in *another* world. We're *beside* ourselves rather than *in* ourselves. We're energised in a manic way, prepared to do the impossible for each other.'

I asked her about Jacob's first meeting with Rachel.

'Rachel would be your classical *anima* figure, the woman of your dreams, the one you have 'known' for thousands of years, the one who walks into a crowded room, your eyes meet and like walking through a mist, you find yourself heading towards each other, convinced that you are soul mates.'

'It's a peculiar chemistry, isn't it? But what makes it go sour for so many of us?'

Jessie looked at me and held my gaze. 'It's because we are ultimately red-blooded and flawed … we are not gods and goddesses. To pretend otherwise, is to fail each other as human beings.'

Jessie sat down against a rock and massaged her calves. She was humming away quietly to herself. I wondered how much of my soul she carried. What else could account for the feeling that I sometimes had – that even though I knew her well I didn't have a clue who she was? Like Jacob for Rachel, I would have done anything for her.

… Jacob served seven years for Rachel; and they seemed unto him but a few days, for the love he had for her.

'It's beautiful, isn't it,' Jessie said. 'But at the end of the day, what kind of a love was that?' I waited for her to answer her own question. I was intrigued.

140

'It was hardly an earthly love at all, if you ask me,' she continued, 'it was adoration. Jacob had put Rachel up on a pedestal and she unconsciously went along with it. She was probably too young to know better, but in any case, it led to her becoming out of reach … ungrounded … unreal. *She was barren*, we are told. When looked at psychologically, her barrenness alludes to her being out of touch with her creativity. It was drying up!'

'Is that *barrenness* the consequence of living our lives according to the expectations and projections of others?'

'Yes, that's what I mean,' she said. 'And of course, we all like to be adored don't we? But at what cost? At the cost of losing what is authentic in us … our soul? At the cost of losing out on what it means to be truly loved … warts and all?'

'So, Rachel needed to come down off the pedestal?'

'Yes. She needed not only to speak for herself, but to be herself.'

'Do you know that in the story as it is written, Rachel does not utter a single word until she recognises her barrenness?'

I said I didn't know that, but it seemed like a good time to say something.

'Listen to this, Hamish,' she said ignoring my response, 'Rachel's first reported words were … *Give me children or else I die.* Give me what belongs to me. She wanted down off the pedestal. She wanted to be part of a *relationship*. Like old Cain, out of her barrenness came her great cry of grief.'

'In effect, was she not also saying to Jacob, "Look at yourself. Carry your own soul … let me own mine"?'

'Yes,' said Jessie, 'It was a wake-up call for both of them, really. In that statement of intent, Rachel declared her boundaries and it transformed their relationship. It is one thing to be a god-maker, it is another to try to be a god or goddess. That's when it all dries up!'

I tried to imagine Rachel's challenge to Jacob as if it had come from me, a challenge to the mommy's boy regarding my own creativity, that part of me which, if not acknowledged and expressed, would become crusty and haunt me. How many of us had allowed the artist within us to dry up, I wondered?

I imagined the blossoming Rachel in Jessie — a woman in the process of becoming her own person.

27

AND SHE CONCEIVED, and bare a son.

In a fascinating account of the events leading to the cure for Rachel's barrenness, Jessie described the symbolic role of the *Mandragora officinalis* in the new-found fertility of the biblical character. *Mandragora*, also known as the mandrake, is a plant which is found in southern Europe. On a particular harvest day, the story goes, Rachel sees her nephew with a mandrake. For reasons which are not explained, she *has* to have it. It becomes a need of compulsive proportions until, after a deal with her older sister – she permits her an extension of conjugal rights with her husband, Jacob – she claims her prize. We are not told what she did with it, but we are left with no doubt as to what happened the moment she took ownership of it ... *God remembered Rachel ... and opened her womb.*

Referring to the mandrake, Jessie spoke of its belladonna-like properties and of its use through the centuries not only as an emetic, but as a narcotic. She drew attention to its poisonous white flower, but all considered, it was the root that captured her imagination ... and mine. 'The root looks like a small human being,' she said, shaping her hands as if she were moulding the contours of a mannikin. Seeing in the root the essence of a remedy for those who, for whatever reason, are ungrounded or uprooted, she suggested that it was the *medicine* for those who needed to get in touch with their earthiness. I liked that. I remembered what Jessie said about Rachel being up on a pedestal, realising that she was referring to the mandrake as the likely remedy for her barren condition.

But there was more. Jessie saw in the inflammatory, belladonna-like properties of the leaves a reflection of the human capacity not only for anger but for passion also. Turning to its narcotic properties, she alluded to the necessity of sleep and the need for a greater understanding of the nature and language of dreams. And there was its flower … beautiful but poisonous. On the one hand, she saw in this the psychological image of a potency, unique and non-toxic to the one whose creativity is permitted to blossom, but on the other hand slow poison for those whose artistry is unexpressed or second-hand. Finally, she focused on the timing of Rachel's realisation that the mandrake belonged to her.

'It was at the time of the *harvest*,' she emphasised. 'She was *ready* for it. The essence of her creativity was in that plant and she knew it. She had to have it, but it cost her. It meant a certain sacrifice,' she said, alluding to the seemingly unusual deal with her older sister. 'You can read that yourself, Hamish. The significance of it is that to be authentic, to *be who you are*, will cost you. It always involves some kind of sacrifice. But it will cost you more if you don't.'

28

WE HAD BEEN walking very slowly. Thomas and Brian were still below us, but the gap between us had narrowed. From where I was standing I looked back and in the distance below us I could just make out the tents in our camp. They were little specks of colour.

Since our previous short break, we had been climbing for more than an hour and I was thirsty again. Jessie had added fruit-flavoured rehydration salts to the water, which made it quite tasty. I took a couple of deep swigs from the bottle and passed it on to Brian. He drank deeply, which pleased me. 'How're you doing?' I asked.

'Reasonably up to shit,' he said with a wry face. 'But better than yesterday,' he added, burping to relieve himself of brewing stomach gases.

There was a cold wind coming up from the plateau and we all wiggled our way into resting places among the boulders. Jessie closed her eyes. Carol and Helen sat close to each other and chatted quietly. Brian wedged himself between two large rocks while Hugh stretched himself out on a flat face of granite. Thomas and Julius shared a cigarette.

Looking down along the western moorlands of the Shira plateau, I watched as the wind was making wave after wave in the long grass. I soaked up its vastness and its beauty. I pictured myself running through the dancing grasses, on my own, all the way to the northern edge of the plateau, and not being tired at all.

I could see myself on that edge, gazing into the Great Rift Valley and Olduvai Gorge ... to where, arguably, it all began for us ...

★   ★   ★

Not so long ago, in Olduvai Gorge, the two-million-year-old skull of *Homo habilis* was found, the earliest evidence to date of a hominid with a skull that could accommodate a 750 cc brain. This ancient relative, with a skull size comparable to that of a crawling infant, probably spent much of his time on all fours foraging for food. His thumb did not operate independently from his other fingers, which meant that his manual grasp of things was crude.

Later, skulls of around 1 150 cc, a million years more evolved than *Homo habilis*, were unearthed. Without any evidence of a gradual increase in brain capacity, *Homo erectus* had arrived. A hominid that stood up! The human stood erect! I thought of the child who pulls herself up onto her feet, by herself, for the first time ... of what it must have been like to see the world from a new height, from a new perspective. It must have been as frightening as it was exciting. Standing up, it seemed, was not a choice. It was an *urge*.

Other neurological quantum leaps were to follow – no one could ever say that evolution was necessarily slow! The leaps went something like this:

Homo habilis ... 2 000 000 years ago ... skull size – 750 cc
Homo erectus ... 1 000 000 years ago ... skull size – 1 150 cc
Homo sapiens ... 250 000 years ago ... skull size – 1 400 cc
Homo sapiens sapiens ... 40 000 years ago ... skull size 1 500 cc

Every leap in the size of the hominid skull represented a leap in the size of the neurological cortex, that part of the brain without which we would not be able to reflect upon ourselves.

As if in a recapitulating pattern of history, the skull of the human being expands from size *habilis* to size *sapiens sapiens* in just one year of leaving the mother's womb. I saw in this phenomenon two things: on the one hand, an evolutionary urge like the forward-pointing thorn of the *Ziziphus*, to keep moving, to keep looking ahead, and on the other, to stand still, to reflect upon ourselves, like the thorn that curled backwards … to remember where we have come from.

★   ★   ★

It was time for me to get up from my comfortable position in the sun, propped up on my daypack. By the time I got to my feet, I could see that Hugh was way ahead on the upward path. Maybe he wanted to be on his own for a while. Carol and Helen were adjusting their packs and Thomas looked at me with a gentle eye. He did not say anything. Brian heaved himself to his feet and started walking.

'What were you thinking about then, honey?' Jessie asked me. 'You seemed to be light years away.'

I had often been on the receiving end of that statement – 'you're miles away'.

'About two million years,' I answered dryly.

'Was I there with you?' she asked. She did not need an answer.

29

'YOU CAN SEE the silence coming in,' said Hugh poetically. He was watching the mist and the way it was literally feeling its way up through the nooks and the crannies of the mountainside. The silence was immense.

Up ahead and not far from us, a path branched off, curving away toward the south. Thomas told us that it was an alternative path to the summit, by way of the Barranco and Barafu campsites on the high south-west slopes of the Kibo massif. He said that we would pass through Barafu on our way down in two days' time.

Two days' time! It was difficult to comprehend. I remembered having the same feeling at the hotel in Moshi. Now I couldn't imagine one day, let alone two. He might as well have said we would pass through Barafu in two *years'* time. I had never been here before. There was nothing that was familiar to me, no reassuring information for my ego, like 'This is where I am, this is what I'm going to see tomorrow, this is what I can expect.' No, all I was aware of was the starkness of the silent surroundings precipitating a cold sense of immediacy. The present moment loomed larger than I had ever experienced it before. It was as if there was no past or future. There was only *now*! There was only *here*!

I looked down at my boots and saw my feet in relation to the path. So this is where I am, I said to myself. Here! And here! And with the next step, here!

Thomas let out a high-pitched whistle, drawing attention to himself. He said that it was a good time to head back to Shira. It was the turning-point of the day's climb.

★   ★   ★

So this is who we are, I thought – recent hominids on a recent earth, cortical man, the ones with the big mushroom-shaped brains, the ones who are supposedly equipped to reflect upon themselves and their world?

I was getting cynical again, but I did not try to resist it. I continued the dialogue with myself, or was it with Genesis?

Do we belong here? A big part of me said 'maybe' but another part said 'maybe not'. It was difficult to ignore the possibility that we had unconsciously pathologised ourselves on earth, that we had become a disease and that there was something malignant about us. It is what one of the astronauts thought when he looked down at earth from outer space. We have repeatedly turned against our host, against each other and against ourselves. In the name of progress, let alone out of sheer wilfulness, we unwittingly destroy the very things that sustain us. With little or no awareness of a sense of continuity, we do everything desperately – we reproduce, we fight, we blame, we win and we lose … desperately.

Contemplating the greatest of all our imponderable questions, I asked myself, *Who are we?* It seemed highly unlikely that we would ever come close to an answer as long as we were looking for it outside of ourselves.

I looked down along the winding path across the Shira plateau. And then I knew. It was imperative that we came to understand that there were at least two evolutionary paths. An inner one and an outer one, a symbolic one and a 'concrete' one – and that we had to honour both. It was the image of the *Ziziphus* again.

★   ★   ★

I was amazed at how quickly the sky had clouded over. The clouds around us had darkened into a menacing reservoir of rain. The wind had dropped, leaving in its place the peculiar silence

149

that often comes before the heavens open. I had only known that silence in Africa. And then came the unmistakable smell of rain. Suddenly there was a stunning flash of lightning. We hardly had time to register the visual impact of the flash – it must have been close – when the thunder, in full vent, ripped its way out of the clouds. For a moment I felt completely disorientated, almost paralysed by the explosion of sound.

I called to Jessie to stay close to me and my words were hardly out, when the clouds were split by another ferocious dagger of light, unleashing in turn a terrifying explosion of thunder. I was frightened. In an electrical storm this was definitely not the right place to be – out in the open.

'Come with me!' urged Thomas. His forehead had screwed up into a tight frown and his eyes moved rapidly between the slopes above us and the advancing rain on the plateau to the west. 'We must move to those big boulders over there and take shelter until the rain passes,' he called.

The wind had returned with astonishing aggression and the advancing front of rain was upon us. The first drops arrived like water bombs, slapping my back and making small craters as they splashed into the ground.

I was holding Jessie's hand as we negotiated a narrow ravine, close to the boulders to which we were heading. She had a smile on her face. 'This is fun!'

'Like hell,' I answered. 'I nearly wet myself when that lightning struck,' ushering her away from the windward side of the granite outcrop.

The rain came down like a great emptying, reducing the visibility to no more than five or six metres. It was hitting the ground with such force that we would not have been able to hear each other talking if we had wanted to. Even Carol and Helen had been silenced. We were all huddled together, pushing our backs against a curving rock face. Helen cleared her throat nervously and as if the sky itself had demanded the silence, it answered back with a thunderous tongue-lashing.

No one said a word. It seemed that we were playing hide-and-seek with the elements. It was us hominids, little pieces of earth, trying to hide from water, air and fire. Our silence became an unspoken plea to the mountain. 'You *know* who we are. You, too, are a piece of earth,' I muttered.

The narrow ravines had swelled dramatically, and what had been whispering streams minutes before were now raging torrents of water that raced toward the rainforest far below us. The sound of thunder bounced off the peaks, the slopes and the valleys and no one moved. Carol's eyes were closed and I wondered … was that rain coming down her cheek?

I had never been in a situation like that before, so utterly gripped by the indifference, the hostility and the unmistakable honesty of the elements. To say that I felt at one with that mountain and the surrounding landscape would have been ludicrous. That afternoon, the mountain did not give a solitary shit about any of us. We were on our own.

Then as suddenly as it had begun, the rain stopped. The clouds thinned out and the sun peeped through. Apart from the cascading rivulets and the steam rising up from the rain-drenched boulders, who would have thought that less than five minutes ago we were in the middle of a nightmare?

Looking up toward the peak, I wondered how David Joseph was and what Lucas Steyn was doing.

★   ★   ★

In the six-hundredth year of Noah's life, in the second month, the seventeenth day of the month, the same day, were all the fountains of the great deep broken up, and the windows of heaven were opened … And the rain was upon the earth … for there were giants in the land.

★   ★   ★

We had to take care not to descend too quickly on the path, which had become muddy and slippery after the storm. I was glad to have my long walking-stick with me, which I used to test the consistency of the ground ahead and to take up some of my weight as I negotiated the steeper parts on the path.

I thought about the rage of the storm and how small we really are in the spectrum of the elements.

★   ★   ★

Jessie spoke about Noah's story like this:

Sometimes, when the *giants* are in the land, it refers to the feeling you have when you think you're bigger than you actually are, you've got the world by the balls, so to speak. This is a state of ego inflation. You've forgotten where you have come from. Watch it! That's often when the floods come. For others, the *giants* are part of the core of what we have repressed, what we have unconsciously 'forgotten' in our psyche. They become the fuel for the crippling neuroses of our lives. There are times when they have to be confronted. It can be very frightening … David and Goliath stuff. 'Those are the *giants*,' she said.

And then, in a fascinating image, she described a major depressive illness as the modern equivalent of Noah's flood.

The giants can be the nagging clouds of discontent gathering on our horizons, she said. We begin to experience a peculiar kind of uneasiness or dissatisfaction with our lives. Sleep does not come easily. We wake up at two or three in the morning and that's it … we can't go back to sleep. We lie awake until the morning, exhausted, forcing ourselves to get up. Things that usually give us pleasure, no longer do. We don't have the energy to make decisions, and the feeling we have is that our world is closing in. The great floods in our lives, then, represent those *dark nights of the soul* …

'The opening up of the fountains of the deep is a remarkable yet frightening image of a depression, perhaps of psychotic proportions,' Jessie commented. 'Depending on the degree of containment, for some the flood represents a major breakdown. For others a major breakthrough. For both, however, the world will never be the same again.'

I imagined the experience as being an intensely lonely time, when every value, every belief or conviction was challenged and when self-questioning included the issue of one's sanity.

'When there is an *ark*, a safe place in which to weather the storm, a breakthrough is possible,' Jessie said. 'Without one, a breakdown is almost guaranteed.'

'The ark, then, is an outer and an inner phenomenon,' she said. She described an inner space, one of containment where the emotional upheavals that come with life's storms can be integrated, as well as an outer one, a tangible place of containment and safety – a home, a consulting room, a clinic, or a tract of wilderness, maybe a mountain.

And every beast and every creeping thing ... and every fowl and every bird ... went in.

'To survive the dark nights of the soul, we have to bring our animal and animating sides along with us, two by two, the positive and the negative aspects of our instincts, the dual sides of ourselves; the masculine and the feminine, the maybe and maybe not, what we like about ourselves and what we don't. We need to bring along what is oldest and most primal in us – our *wild* side.'

★   ★   ★

The remaining storm clouds were on the horizon. They looked less potent now.

Stopping for a rest, I asked Thomas if there were any animals on the mountain. He shook his head slowly.

'What animals used to be here?' I asked.

He thought about his answer and then shook his head again. He spoke slowly, telling me that his father used to see many animals ... lion, buffalo, elephant, antelope and many wild pigs.

'They are all gone now,' he said. 'They have been taken by the poachers and the hunters. It has all changed.'

Hugh had been listening intently. I knew how he felt about animals and modern methods of hunting and the amount of money involved ... that the animal has no chance.

'Did you know that the word *animal* comes from the Latin and later the old French word *anima*, meaning "breath" or "soul"?' Hugh asked me.

'That's interesting, Jessie was talking about that yesterday,' I said.

'When we begin to lose animals and wild areas as we are doing now, or when a species becomes extinct, I believe something in us dies, also. Maybe we suffer a loss of soul … depressing, isn't it?' he muttered.

I thought about Jessie's image of depression. Was depression linked to a loss of connection with what was wild or unrefined in us? Was this why some people need to go into the wilderness?

★   ★   ★

No one spoke during the final hour of our descent to Shira camp. The silence was palpable. In it were the traces of distant lightning and the sound of thunder. None of us had ever been in a storm like that. None of us had ever before felt quite so small. The only sounds were of footsteps that scraped against the rocks on the winding pathway.

The porters who had stayed behind at the camp came out to greet us when we arrived. Some of them were laughing and began to taunt Thomas, but he did not react. They knew what had happened. It was as if they had chosen to stay at the camp.

Thomas saw us to our tents and then he told us that he would bring hot tea and biscuits. When he left, he headed toward the fire where the porters were standing. Those who had been taunting him formed a loose circle around him as he walked. They laughed and slapped their hands on their thighs, intermittently pointing to the mountain. I watched Thomas stop and point towards our tents. For a while there was silence around him and then they began to laugh again.

Did Thomas know? Did he do this on purpose, taking us into the storm like that? Was it some kind of rite of passage that we should experience our insignificance on this mountain in such a way? I turned to Hugh.

'Can I have one of your cigarettes, please?'

★   ★   ★

The dark night of the soul can be a long one.

And the waters prevailed upon the earth an hundred and fifty days …

'That's about as long as untreated depression lasts,' said Jessie.

30

JESSIE AND I had dozed off in our tent.

'Are you guys awake?' It was Hugh.

'There's some supper on the table,' he said.

I opened my eyes. It was a quarter to six … Kilimanjaro time.

I didn't want to get out of my sleeping-bag. I wanted to be somewhere else, anywhere where the sun was shining and where I could sleep.

The supper 'table' was a large boulder with a smooth and slightly sloping surface. The usual plastic cover with the floral design on it was used as the tablecloth – a little touch of class in the African alpine desert. Knives, forks and side plates were neatly arranged.

On the menu was macaroni and cheese as a main course, followed by pineapple slices and coffee. The stodgy macaroni looked bullet-proof but tasted good. The two alpine chats that had been bobbing around the night before and again at breakfast were back again.

Brian wasn't eating.

Suddenly the sun came out from below the western cloud line, changing the evening from a grey hue to a pink and golden glow. Jessie suggested we take a short walk before it got dark. Warmly dressed, we headed out on the path that leads toward Shira Cathedral.

'Let's walk to that ridge,' she said, pointing to a cluster of rocks that looked like a dragon's backbone.

It took us about twenty minutes to reach the ridge, from where, looking back, we could see our campsite spotlighted in a solitary column of sunlight. Beyond that, outside the sunbeam, the earth was dark, and beyond that Kilimanjaro displayed herself in pinks and whites.

Because of the fading light, I positioned my camera on a large rock and manually reduced the shutter speed to permit as much light as possible to enter. I took two shots and then nodded my appreciation to the mountain.

On the way back to the camp we took a side path which led through an area where black, glass-like stones lay scattered. I identified them as pieces of volcanic rock called obsidian. I had never before seen stones so black. I picked up several pieces, feeling the texture between my thumb and forefinger. They also felt heavier than they looked. Their volcanic origin reminded me of my father's ashes. They too seemed to have volcanic significance. Gravel-like and flecked with black and white, they were not ordinary ashes. They seemed to carry the signatures of ancient mountains and of the sun. In those ashes, as in the blackness of the obsidian, the sun had gone back to where it had come from.

★   ★   ★

By the time Jessie and I reached the campfire, the sun had already ducked down behind Mount Meru. Carol and Helen had come to join us. They stood with Hugh and Brian in a semicircle around the fire, all of them staring into the flames, their hands deep in their pockets and their shoulders hunched up. The wind was brisk enough to contribute a chill factor to the night.

Hugh was talking about some of his experiences with hyenas in Botswana. Helen was repulsed at Hugh's enthusiasm for the spotted creatures.

'I used to feel the same,' said Hugh, 'until I went and found out for myself. I discovered the hyena is probably the most intelligent of all the wild animals. Speak to anyone who has had prolonged contact with them, and they will tell you that the negative things we say about them are unfounded and unfair.'

'In other words, we impose on the hyenas the very qualities we don't like in ourselves?' I asked, more aware now of projections.

'Exactly,' Hugh responded. 'I took back everything that I'd said about them. To me they are beautiful. A hyena is what it is. What you see is what you get – nothing more, nothing less. The hyena does not need us humans to justify its existence.'

Something made me turn around and I looked out into the darkness to see three lights slowly coming towards us. At first I wondered if they were the Italians coming down late from the acclimatisation hike and then, as the trio came closer, I recognised what I thought was David Joseph's red anorak.

'I think we may have a problem here,' I said, turning to Jessie. 'I'd better go and see if they need some help.' Hugh came with me.

An African porter in the group whistled and I whistled back. A short duet of whistling ensued and then I made out the white face in the trio that emerged from the darkness beyond the camp. David was sandwiched between the two men who had descended with him. They were assistant guides from Lucas Steyn's group. David saw me and with a twisted smile on his face, as if to apologise, he made a thumbs-down gesture with his free hand, the other hand clutching his flashlight. His face was pale and drawn and his eyes lay deep in their sockets. He was clearly in need of fluids and medical attention.

By then, Thomas and a group of porters had arrived to see what was happening and I could see the concern on their faces as they assessed the situation. Thomas said something in Swahili and one of our porters turned and ran to the main camp.

I was relieved to hear David say, 'I actually feel a bit better than I was a few hours ago.'

'That's good … Come and rest next to the fire while we organise a drip.'

'Thanks a lot.' He let out a deep breath. 'You won't believe it, but I thought I was going to die up there. It was all I wanted to do. I was hurling my heart out,' he complained, referring to the nausea and vomiting that came with altitude sickness. 'I just wanted to die,' he repeated.

David sipped slowly at the bottle of rehydration fluid while I set up the vacolitre of intravenous dextrose fluid. It was the only one we had, but he was the one who needed it.

I wondered what was going on in Brian's mind. He hadn't said a word and I could see him watching David sipping from the water bottle. Like me, he was probably wondering if he was having a preview of his own fate.

'It's ready now,' said Thomas pointing to the bell-shaped tent that had been erected next to ours. One of the guides who had accompanied David down to Shira had brought David's tent with him.

'Why don't you sleep in our tent?' Jessie suggested. 'We've got plenty of space and, besides, it'll be a lot warmer with the three of us together.'

'I think that's a good idea, David,' I said. 'We can put our backpacks into your tent and that will give us all the space we need. I would like to keep an eye on you anyway.'

I could see the relief on his face as he looked into the dying flames of our campfire. Maybe the relief came from the dextrose in his system, but I think if it was me, the last thing that I would have wanted that night was to spend it alone.

'Are you sure that's okay?' he asked.

The wind was picking up again and the sound in the distance was unmistakable. What was left of the day's unseasonal rain was heading across the Shira plateau toward us.

★   ★   ★

For David Joseph, the worst was over. Things would get better.

'The dark night of the soul is like that,' said Jessie, a little later. 'You wonder how long it is going to take before sunlight returns and the ground beneath your feet will feel solid again. You begin to reach out into a dark world, convinced that there is no hope … no end to the darkness. Dying becomes a viable option … and then you begin to wish you were dead. And then, one day, you

158

know that *something* in you is different – the tide begins to turn. That happened to Noah.'

And the dove came unto him in the evening; and lo, in her mouth there was an olive leaf plucked off: so Noah knew that the waters were abated from off the earth.

★   ★   ★

Once the drip was complete, I removed the needle from the vein and dressed it with some plaster. The rain was beating down on the 'fly' sheet and we all got ourselves into our sleeping-bags.

David was the first to fall asleep. His breathing was just audible, coming from my right side. It was deep and even. Jessie searched for my hand under our sleeping-bag and gave it a squeeze. 'I think he's away,' she said.

A part of me envied him. He was on his way down now. He had gone as far as his body would let him and you couldn't go farther than that. David Joseph had probably pushed himself farther than he had ever gone before. That took courage. So what if he didn't get to the top. Where was that anyway?

Staring up at the canopy of the tent, I wondered how I would be feeling in twenty-four hours' time.

I tried to picture the final campsite, eight hundred metres from the top, but I couldn't. Instead I saw myself wide awake, waiting for the midnight call to begin the last climb. I pictured the steel tins with the ashes and the 'wee book' as my father had called it.

★   ★   ★

This was my dream on that third night.

I was climbing along a very narrow path somewhere in a high mountainous wilderness. I could hear the grass swishing and I could feel the wind in my hair. I looked up and saw a huge rock in the near distance. In profile, the rock looked like a human face. There was something Celtic, something Bushman, something Indian about the face. It was alive, but it would not look at me. It gazed instead into the valleys way below. The profile could have been that of my father.

I woke up, wrestling with the dream. He was here, I thought. He was all around me. 'So this is where you are …'

159

31

THE EARLY MORNING light had silently crept into our tent but it was the rustling sound of David's sleeping-bag as he tried to get himself out of it that woke me. I looked at him very clinically, before speaking. His eyes were a little puffy but I did not want to interpret that as necessarily being a negative sign because it was exactly how I looked in the mornings. His face was pale yellow contrasting with the black stubble of his three-to-four-day-old beard.

'Morning,' I said to him in a low voice. 'How're you doing?'

He nodded his head slowly and then whispered, 'Okay. It's just the headache.'

'How's the nausea?' I asked.

'That seems to be okay now,' he said, prodding himself in the stomach.

Pulling himself out of his sleeping-bag, he tucked his shirt into his jeans. Apart from his boots, he had slept in the same clothes that he had been wearing the day before. His thick socks had slipped down over his feet and they hung over his toes like limp wrists. He pulled them up and then put on his boots without speaking. Jessie, who had woken up in the meantime, watched him in silence.

'I'll come and join you,' I said, wriggling my way out of my bag. I hobbled out into the brisk morning air. It was light, but the sun had not yet reached us. It was busy warming up the eastern slopes of Kibo.

David and I walked down and away from the tents toward some large boulders where we could empty our bladders out of view of the campsite. Together, we peed onto the soft moss that carpeted the ground around the granite boulders. Steam rose up from the ground where warm rivulets of urine soaked into the cold moss. I watched the steam curl and finger its way into nothingness, exactly as the huge, animated banks of mist behaved on the mountain.

The loss of body heat from emptying my bladder caused my body to shiver momentarily – one of those 'somebody is walking over my grave' shivers.

A shiver is a physiological phenomenon caused by the rapid sliding of muscle fibres, one on top of the other. This friction generates heat, which is what the body needs.

Walking back to the tents, I asked David about Lucas Steyn.

'I remember what you told me at Machame camp and how you'd been forced to keep moving,' I said. 'Did he ease up on you at all the next day?'

'Well, it took a long time, but I think he got the message yesterday afternoon.' The tone of David's voice was philosophical.

'You mean he had to wait until you were too ill to continue before he slowed down?' I could feel myself getting angry at the thought of Lucas Steyn urging everyone on like racehorses.

'Well, not really,' said David, catching me by surprise, pulling the reins on my irritation. 'He knew that I was not well from the first day already, but I don't think that worried him. He kept telling me that I'd get over it. What slowed him down yesterday was not so much me, but that the altitude had started to get to *him*! He developed a cough during the early afternoon and it got to the point where he was forced to rest. By late afternoon, he was not looking so good. At that stage, I was vomiting every twenty to thirty minutes and I knew the climb was over for me.'

'Who helped you in your decision to call it a day?'

'Vincent, the guide … The one who accompanied me last night. He said it was not good for me to continue, otherwise I was going to get sick. How's that for understatement? Vincent made the decision for me. Someone had to tell me *that's enough!*'

'What did Lucas and the others say?'

'I think that they were relieved. Lucas, who was coughing away when I told him I was leaving, had an unforgettable look in his eyes. It was the look of someone who was scared. He did not have any hold on me any longer. It was strange … I actually felt sorry for him.'

'I think you've been incredibly courageous, David. I just wonder how you would have fared if you'd been given the chance to take it easy and to acclimatise.'

'I'm sorry,' I went on, 'but I think Lucas Steyn is an arsehole. Maybe there's some kind of mountain justice at work, hearing what you're saying about his condition. He could be in trouble, you know.'

'Maybe,' said David. 'But he's a tough customer. He'll probably drag himself to the top. Anyway, at the end of the day I was the one who chose to stay with him and the rest of the group, instead of coming with you. Maybe things would have been different. It's funny how things work out. I kind of hoped that he would shit off. But now he doesn't bother me. That look in his eyes said it all. I was sick, but I was not scared. I feel okay about going back now. It just wasn't my time.'

I put my hand on his shoulder and squeezed it.

'Where were you on the mountain when you turned back?'

'We were just beyond Lava Rock, a massive volcanic slab. You'll see it today sometime … there's a profile on it that looks like a human face. That's where the storm hit us. And that's when Vincent said *Enough.*'

Lava Rock? A human profile? Was this some kind of dream?

★   ★   ★

Vincent and the other guide came up to where we were tidying up the breakfast area. It had been a good breakfast of our usual cornflakes, scrambled eggs, toast and tea. They had been waiting for us to finish our meal.

I was struck by the gentleness of his voice when he spoke to David, who was standing next to Hugh and Jessie. 'Mister David,' he said, 'it's a good time to leave.'

'I'm ready,' said David reaching over to where he had placed his daypack.

'Cheers, chaps,' he said, briefly making eye contact with us. 'I'll have some cold beers ready for you when you get back to the hotel on Friday. And thanks for all your help.'

'Hold it!'

I turned round to see where the voice came from. It was a firm command and I could hear it reverberating in my head ... '*Hold it!*' It was Brian.

'I'm going with you,' he said, looking at David.

We were all momentarily stunned. His bag was already packed. His sunglasses covered his eyes and he stood in the manner of someone who knew where he was going.

'Sorry, guys, but I think this mountain's had enough of me. I wasn't ready for her ... maybe another time ...' The ensuing silence seemed endless. It was as if the whole world had slowed down. What could we say? Brian knew himself better than we did. Hugh just stared at him. He knew that once Brian had made up his mind, that was it. He then walked up and put his arms around him. Jessie followed and held him tightly. 'Take care,' she said, brushing back her tears. What else could she say? Words of protest began to form around my mouth, but nothing came out. Then I did the same. I hugged him. Swallowing hard, my throat ached. I could not get myself to believe what was happening. It was all too quick. Thomas nodded his head slowly. He was not surprised.

With one last wave, they moved off. In silence we watched them walking slowly downwards through the dip that led to a nearby stream. My eyes followed them up the rise to where the path began to stretch its way toward a ridge after which we would not see them again. When they arrived at the ridge, I ceremoni-ously held up my hand to wave, just in case Brian or David turned to acknowledge us, but they kept on walking. Not once did they look back. We stood in silence long after they had disappeared. Then Thomas cleared his throat.

★ ★ ★

Not to look back, but to keep looking ahead has become a widely accepted admonition in our society. Put the past behind you. Forget the bad times. How did this fit in with the message of the thorns of the *Ziziphus* – remembering where we have come from – I wondered.

'Can you remember what happened to Lot's wife?' Jessie asked.

'The one who turned into salt?' I responded. 'What was that all about?'

'*Escape for your life; look not behind thee,*' Jessie quoted. '*But his wife looked back … and she became a pillar of salt.*'

Jessie said this story related to the difficulties that some of us have when we get stuck in our past, unable to recognise the difference between *remembering* the past without getting *stuck* in it. She reminded me of the cliché 'to forgive and forget', where the two verbs were said in the same breath. 'Forgetting and forgiving do not necessarily follow,' she said. 'For a start, it's impossible to forget. The psyche won't allow it. What happened to Lot's wife happens to us. Instead of giving our memories a sense of continuity or purpose, we are inclined to look back on them as stumbling-blocks in our lives, as the reasons why we could never move on. We look back on the betrayals and the disappointments in our lives and we *live* there. We become pillared in the salt of our wounds. We become bitter. Forgiveness becomes impossible.'

'What we could try to do, however, is to *re-member* the trauma of our past,' she added. 'We can *re-member* the betrayals, the rejections and put the memories together again, in a different way, so that we can live *with* them. Maybe then, but not before then, can we begin to try to do the seemingly impossible – we can try to forgive.'

'Clients often come to therapy for this reason,' she said. 'They feel stuck, unable to come to terms with their past. It is as if their

164

past has become their fate, and, as you know, fate and destiny are not the same thing. They have to do something about it. Interestingly, the cure is in the analogy of mining. We have to go in and *mine* the salt. The salt is the sodium chloride of our juices … it's in our tears, in our blood and our sweat. We have to bring it to the surface. Then we can get in touch with it. Only then, can we re-moisten it, so that our lives can flow again.'

I thought about the political implications of Jessie's analysis and of Brian's thoughts. How many people in my country would continue to remain bitter … pillared in the past … white and black?

Forgiveness was about another level of consciousness.

★   ★   ★

And then we were three.

I took a photograph of Hugh's and Brian's tent. It was perched on the rim of a ledge from which there was an unhindered view across to a middle-distant slope of rugged peaks, one of which was the majestic Shira Cathedral. Beyond that was the bluish-grey Mount Meru and a long way below, the rainforest and the flats, the everyday world of the people of Tanzania. Perched as high as it was, looking out onto the world of mortals, it could have been the tent of a guru. I imagined a sign on the front of the tent reading, '*I hope you find what you are looking for.*' I figured that my cynical humour was a defence against the tenderness of the lump in my throat. I did not enjoy having to say goodbye to Brian like that. Saying goodbye to David was different. I was prepared for that.

I wondered if I was prepared for what lay ahead.

Inclining his head upward and toward the glaciers, Thomas said that it was time for us to go.

'How long will it take us to get to the Lava Rock?' asked Hugh.

I watched Thomas's face as he turned to look at the mountain, the sky and then at Hugh. I silently predicted what Thomas's answer would be. I knew it would not be a direct answer, like 'four or five hours', and I was right.

'It will not take very long,' he said.

Hugh looked at me. 'Why are you smiling?' he asked.

'Nothing … I was just thinking about something … I'll tell you later.'

'Tell me now,' he implored.

'What do you think of this: *Nobody is having a better time than you or me?*'

'Just say that again.'

'Nobody in the world is ever having a better time than you or me,' I repeated. 'It's an attitude.' I said. 'It's the one that's going to get me to the top, because if it isn't true, then I'm not going to make it.'

Hugh thought about it for a while and then looked at me. 'I'll go with that.'

The porters were still eating their breakfast when we trudged our way past them, heading toward the path that would take us to Lava Rock and Kibo. They didn't seem to be in any hurry at all, sitting around their open fire. I greeted them and they greeted us back. Compared with the day before, there was little laughter from their fireside. Maybe they were feeling our loss. Maybe some of them had lost money on Brian. I wondered if they had taken a few bets among themselves. If so, the odds were clearly shortening. What did they think of Jessie's or my chances? Hugh, I thought, was our safest bet.

It was going to be a long day, retracing yesterday's steps to the Barranco turn-off, from where we had turned round, descending into that hell of a storm. We would be heading up past that into new country.

★   ★   ★

Hugh and I found ourselves walking together again. This time he was a few steps behind me.

'How're you doing?' I asked, knowing that he must be missing his friend.

'I don't know. Do you think that Brian's okay?'

'He's probably got a lot more common sense than you and me and I think he made the right decision.'

'I'm glad you said that.'

It must have been the extra day we spent acclimatising, but I felt reasonably strong. On the other hand it could have been the familiarity of the path, knowing more or less what was coming up around the next bend. For the time being, I knew where I was going. I felt a sense of containment knowing the surroundings. I felt a kind of peace. Maybe the rocks and this path that we had walked on yesterday knew me.

Looking back, I could see where the campfire had been put out. The first of the remaining porters were heading toward our path, carrying their assigned loads of equipment on their heads.

'Shira was a good place,' I said.

Hugh looked back and nodded. He was much more focused on what was up ahead.

'This time tomorrow ...' he mused.

'God! That's right. We should be at the top.'

'Seems like a lifetime away, doesn't it?'

'You took the words out of my mouth,' I muttered.

I thought about Brian. In a way I envied him. He had a far better sense of his limitations than I did. He knew that he had gone as far as he could and he accepted it. It was as though he didn't mind not getting there ... to the top. He had gone as far as he had needed to and that was okay.

★   ★   ★

Looking down the mountain from where we were, I thought of the different places and situations we had been in – the changing vegetation, the altitude, the changing climate and the mountain that played hide-and-seek. I thought of how our lives are like constant initiations, constant transitions from one phase into another, from one grouping of people to another, from one country to another.

★   ★   ★

Abraham was told ... *Get thee out of thy country, and from thy kindred, and from thy father's house, unto a land that I will shew thee.*

I thought of my children back home and of their friends. I thought of the 'war cry' of their adolescence – 'We will not be like our fathers or our mothers.' The shoe was on the other foot. What my children were trying to tell me, I think, was this: 'I would like your blessing, but I do not need your approval.' They were also saying, 'You are a part of my fate, Dad, but you're not my destiny.'

'Adolescence is the wilderness phase, the transition between the Eden of childhood and a beckoning "new Jerusalem" of adulthood. These phases represent patterns of consciousness in the evolution of the god-maker,' said Jessie. 'Every stage in the development of consciousness is *the land that I will shew thee*. They are important stages, but we can't stay there for long. Again, the psyche won't permit it. The forward-pointing thorn of the *Ziziphus* comes into the picture. The envelope has to be stretched, as they say. We have to keep moving. The Abraham in us knows that. So does the Adam and so do the other characters in our personal Genesis.'

★   ★   ★

Our heavily laden porters breezed past us. Two of them were singing in rhythm with their steps. Another couple were talking to each other at the top of their voices, even though they were only a metre or two apart. They seemed happy. Maybe it was because they knew that they were not going the whole way to the top. Only Thomas and Julius would be going further. By sunrise the next day, they would be well on their way down to the base camp on the edge of the rainforest.

I thought of my father and William Phiri having been on the same path forty years previously. I remembered him telling me how reluctant he had been at times to carry on and then the dream image of the face on the rock and the sound of his voice came back. I felt a surge of energy in my legs. 'Is that you, James Malcolm?' It was as if he was walking next to me. His image was vivid. He was young. He was smiling. He was my father. There was no clutter about him; no excess baggage in his wardrobe or in his speech. He was almost Spartan in a lifestyle which was complemented by the generosity of his spirit. I remembered him as an incredibly giving person. He showed a respect for every living thing and it showed in the way that he cared for his clothes, his shoes, his pencils – in fact – all the little things he owned. He was a hard act to follow. Maybe that was another reason why I had been angry with him.

'I'm not like that,' I muttered. 'I'm not like you, James Malcolm, although sometimes I wish I were. And yes, I think I do have a respect for all living things, as you did, I do take care of my things, but, somehow, you seemed less "cluttered" than me. How did you do it?'

Silence.

In the years immediately following his death, I often talked to him. It was as though he was right there. I greeted him, asking him how he was getting on; that sort of thing. I would tell him a few things about what I had been doing. I *knew* he was listening.

It had been a long time since I had done that. I couldn't help it.

★　　　★　　　★

'That's it,' said Jessie.

'That's what?' I asked.

'The path to Barranco … there it goes to the right.'

Good God … we were there already! What happened to the time? We sat down on a clump of boulders close to the place from where we had turned around the day before. I noticed there was nothing graceful about the way I lowered myself onto the boulder that I had chosen to sit on, plopping down onto it quite heavily. I sat there for a while and then groaned as I twisted the backpack off my shoulders. I was pooped. Jessie had already taken a few mouthfuls from the water bottle and passed it on to me.

'That's better,' I said.

'How're you doing, Jessie?' I asked, passing the open water bottle back to her, indicating to her to drink some more.

'It's just the headache,' she said. 'It doesn't let up.'

'Do you want to take something for it?' I asked.

'No thanks. I'll see how it goes … but if it gets worse or if it's still there tonight, I'll take a couple of painkillers.'

'Do you know what I'd like to be doing now ?' I asked.

'What?'

'Sleep!' I answered. 'I'd like to curl up and sleep for a few days.'

I looked up to see if Kibo Peak was still keeping an eye on us, but it had disappeared behind a vast high curtain of cloud. I could feel that it was colder than the day before and for the first time I put on my gortex windbreaker during the day. I wiggled my feet to test how cold they were and decided they were okay.

'It's going to get colder from here.' Hugh shivered.

Thomas was standing up and looking past us, as if deep in thought. We had learned that whenever he did that he was telling us it was time to get moving. I was reluctant to get up and for a while I pretended that I had not seen him.

I felt my pulse. Even though I had been resting, my heart was beating at a shade under a hundred and twenty. I took a deep breath and breathed out as I stood up, swinging my pack across my shoulders once again. It struck me that my movements were becoming increasingly deliberate.

Hugh was smoking a cigarette and the look on his face told us that he didn't want to be hurried.

'Are you okay?' I asked.

He didn't answer but nodded his head in a hint of affirmation.

Jessie and I waited for him and the three of us took our first steps into unknown territory.

For a while, I settled into a comfortable rhythm of two steps for each inward breath and another two for the outward ones.

I spent a lot of the time looking down at the path. It just seemed more comfortable that way. From time to time, like a periscope, I lifted my head out of my shoulders and scanned the terrain. We were now in true alpine desert. There was scarcely a shrub to be seen and the notion that we were walking on the moon was not far-fetched. It would make a good photograph, I thought, but I put it off until we took our next break.

Way up ahead, I saw the path taking a wide circular route, almost back-tracking as it coursed its way over a high ridge. Our porters were already on that ridge, looking like little ants walking in a line one behind the other. They were easily an hour ahead of us. I wished we were there and then one of Rilke's poems came to me:

> *I live my life in growing orbits,*
> *which move out over the things of the world.*
> *Perhaps I can never achieve the last,*
> *but that will be my attempt.*
> *I am circling around God, around the ancient tower,*
> *and I have been circling for a thousand years,*
> *and I still don't know if I am a falcon, or a storm,*
> *or a great song.*

★   ★   ★

'You know why I'm here, don't you? I'm following in your fucking footsteps!' I called out loudly.

'What's that?' Jessie was startled by the volume and nature of my outburst. Hugh's expression told me that he was about to ask the same thing.

'I'm talking to my father,' I shouted. Hugh and Jessie looked at each other quizzically. They were probably wondering if the altitude had finally got to me.

'I'm okay. I'm just getting something off my chest.'

'And you know what I'm carrying in my bloody backpack, don't you?' I continued.

Silence.

'It's that stupid book of yours, as well as your ...' I held back on the ashes because Jessie and I were the only ones there who knew that I had them.

I had never spoken to my father like that before, alive or dead. It felt okay.

'Listen, James Malcolm,' I hissed. 'I know you are here, somewhere. I didn't come here just to have a go at you. And neither did I come because I thought you might approve. I came here because I needed to get to know *you* a little better and maybe you could get to know *me* a little better, too. Look! Here I am carrying these bits and pieces of you in my backpack.' Suddenly the ridiculousness of the image I had just conjured up struck home and I began to giggle. Then, with my face turned toward the sky, I began to laugh and cry at the same time. Tears were rolling down my cheeks. I am sure that Jessie, Hugh and Thomas thought it was all over for me, but I didn't care. When I had settled, I mumbled one more thing to my father, 'Why did you have to bloody well die when you did?' I picked up a stone from the path and threw it into the sky. There was a lot of anger carried in that stone. It was as if I was throwing back a part of what belonged to him. I watched as it curved its way back to earth and as it landed, coming to rest close by, I felt better.

★   ★   ★

As I figured, it took a little more than an hour to get to the ridge where I had last seen the porters. From there I could see Lava Rock. It was a massive, rectangular granite monolith. The thought of it rupturing out of the belly of its volcanic mother and then tumbling through the sky like a giant meteorite into the earth to where it now stood was in the realm of ancient nightmares.

It was about two kilometres away, which meant another hour or so – at least!

Two k's is not far on the flats, but at that altitude and the thirty-degree slope all the way to where it stood, it translated into another mind-time set altogether.

I had long since lost interest in my surroundings, quite satisfied to focus instead on my feet. I composed a short mantra to help keep me going. It went: 'Here-for-the-left-foot … There-for-the-right.' Almost hypnotised by it, I chanted my way to Lava Rock.

'Hey!' It was Hugh, shaking me out of my half-sleep. I looked up and there it was, right behind him – the huge granite lump itself.

There was nothing like it on the rest of the mountain. Its eastern face was like a black mirror in its sheerness. I made a tired attempt to acknowledge it, but it refused to speak to me. I didn't care. I had already lost most of my sense of kinship with the mountain anyway.

At that moment Lava Rock meant only one thing to me. It was just another milestone, just another orbit.

I wondered if it was here that my father had wrestled with the urge to turn back?

Taking into account the wind-chill factor, it was below freezing where we were.

Jessie asked me how I was and I said, 'Fine.' She knew that I was not being honest.

'How're you?' I inquired.

'I've felt better before … Just a bit nauseous,' she said with a look that betrayed her anxiety. She held my eyes for what seemed a long time and then I pointed to a wooden toilet not far from us.

'That must be the highest long-drop in Africa,' I said, trying to be cheerful. 'Whoever goes in there plonks ice.'

Thomas came up to where Jessie and I were sitting. 'You have come a long way,' he declared. It was the first time that I had been verbally reassured by Thomas. Up until then it was his presence that did it.

★   ★   ★

It would seem that Abraham had come quite a long way since he heeded that great inner voice and got himself out of his father's country, taking on a new name and a new identity. Abram became Abraham. He was a *different* person.

'Inner work does that to you,' said Jessie. 'You become a different person. You see things from a different perspective … and it is not always pleasant.'

Like Adam, Abraham *named* his wife … Sarah … it was a symbolic act, an affirmation of *soul*.

Energised by what I felt was a changing relationship with my own father, that I could curse him and laugh with him, I warmed to Abraham's courage to challenge God over the possible destruction of the divided cities of Sodom and Gomorrah.

'*Wilt thou also destroy the righteous with the wicked?*' he challenged.

'Abraham could not have done this if he did not know those twin cities in *himself*,' said Jessie. 'He understood what it was like to be *divided*, but he was not prepared to destroy what was innocent in him, or in others. He said, "No!"'

32

THOMAS SAID THAT we had about an hour and a half to go before we reached the campsite at Arrow Glacier. I was not reassured. Arrow Glacier was where we would snatch a few hours' sleep before making our midnight ascent to view the sunrise from the top of Africa.

I scanned the sky for Kibo Peak, but it wasn't there. It had been hiding for most of the day. So had the glaciers.

Setting off from Lava Rock, the first stretch was on a downward path into a dip and then upward onto a steep winding incline to another ridge on the cloud line. Even though it was a short stretch, it was a relief to be walking downhill for a change. It took a lot of the strain out of the flexor muscles of my legs.

The path soon flattened out and then we were into ascent mode again. The large muscles of my calves and thighs felt disconnected from me and they began to quiver like jelly.

My legs were in revolt and I stopped right in my tracks. I hoped no one wanted to pass me, because I didn't think my legs would permit me to move. They would have to walk around me!

No one passed me. Jessie and Hugh had also come to a dead stop. It was not necessary to ask them about their legs.

After a minute or two I felt better and with the help of my stick I levered my way forward. I looked back to see if Jessie was okay and beyond her I caught a glimpse of the southern face and profile of Lava Rock.

It felt like a spear going into my chest. The image of the dream came rushing in. It was the profile of a Celtic face.

He was here!

Taking a breath, I said to Jessie, 'Take a look at that profile on the southern edge of Lava Rock. Can you make out a face?'

She scrutinised the rock for a while and then said, 'Yes, it looks like the profile of a man. Where have I seen that face before?'

'It's him,' I whispered, but Jessie didn't hear me.

★   ★   ★

I composed another mantra. It went like this …

Breathe in – STEP left – and – out – and – breathe in – and – STEP right – and – out.

I put it to music and it sounded like this …

N kosi sike LEL 'i Af – ri ka …

These were the Nguni words for 'God bless Africa'. I blessed Africa. And then the blizzard hit us.

★   ★   ★

Clambering over the top of a steep incline, I immediately felt the wind stinging into my face. I hadn't realised how sheltered we had been on the upward pull. Peering through my eyelashes, I could see a huge tumbling black cloud heading towards us. It was like a tidal wave.

'It's going to snow,' Thomas informed us without any trace of alarm. Meanwhile Jessie had gone behind some boulders and I could hear her heaving. I went to her and found her looking flushed and tearful. She had been vomiting.

'It leaves a lousy taste in your mouth, doesn't it?' I put my arms around her.

'Is there anywhere else you would rather be?' I teased.

She smiled faintly and shook her head.

The black cloud that we had seen advancing toward us enveloped us in a swirling display of sleet and snow. What was once black had become white. It was an amazing scene. There was something homeopathic about a black cloud filled with whiteness, I thought. You didn't know it until you have been into it and

176

through it. It was a kind of remedy for when we have to confront the storms in our lives. I mulled over the potions of the snake, the mandrake, the obsidian and, now, the image of white in black.

Inner work would seem to be mostly homeopathic, I thought. It is about images and our capacity to *imagine*.

Bitterly cold, I wondered if we were going to take shelter from the sleet coming at us front-on. I looked to see how Thomas was reacting to it but he didn't seem to be phased. Gesturing with his hand and his head, he urged us on. 'We are almost there,' he said, referring to Arrow Glacier. And so, our heads and bodies bent forward, we kept going.

The rhythm of my breathing had changed completely and I was now taking two breaths between every step, stopping for a rest after twenty steps. I could feel the heaviness of my eyelids. If only I could sleep for a few minutes, I thought, then I would be fine. My legs seemed to have got stronger; it was the incoming tide of sleep that I was then battling against. I wondered when the blizzard would stop, and suddenly, as if my thought had been a command, it did. The silence and the stillness were incredible.

Jessie was just behind me. 'Are you okay?' she asked. 'For the last while, you've been dragging your feet.'

I did not want to tell her just how desperately I wanted to sleep so I turned to her and casually said, 'I'm just taking it easy.'

'You look like you're going to fall asleep on your feet,' she said.

'Let me know when I start snoring,' I teased. 'I don't want to wake anyone up.'

The clouds around were rapidly dispersing, breaking up like ghostly ballet dancers, pirouetting as they vanished into nowhere. The sun had broken through, quickly turning the blanket of ice and snow around us into a scatter of glistening mirrors.

'We must get to that ridge there,' said Thomas. 'It's not far.'

I heard him, but I was not listening. Instead, I was engaged in some heavy dialogue with myself ... 'Keep going ... hang in there ... One step at a time. You're nearly there ... just one more sleep ... not far now ... this time tomorrow ... The ashes ... the book … You're taking it back for Dad … to where it belongs … the top.'

I looked up to see the glaciers and the last eight hundred metres of Kilimanjaro's steep upper slopes in full view, brilliantly illuminated from the west. I felt as if I could reach out and touch it, so clear was the air.

Thomas waited for me to reach him and then, gesturing to the mountain peak, he said, 'That is a *very* beautiful sight.' He rolled the 'r' in 'very'. Had I not known better, the accent could have come from somewhere in the west of Scotland.

Hearing him speak like that did something to me. Like the mist that had lifted off the mountain, any thoughts that I had previously had of turning back vanished. I was in another orbit.

'Magnificent,' I said, slowly shaking my head from side to side in awe of the silent spectacle in front of us.

'Look there,' he said, pointing down and away from Kibo Peak. I followed his outstretched arm to see what he was showing us, and there it was – our nomadic village of bell-shaped tents, below Arrow Glacier. Some of the tents were out of the sunlight, shadowed by large boulders still covered with snow from the blizzard.

'I know what I'm going to do when I get there,' said Jessie, breathing heavily.

'So do I and I bet I'll be asleep before you.'

I wondered how Hugh was. Since Lava Rock we had hardly spoken. We had all been quiet, wrapped up in our own thoughts. Hugh was looking at me when my eyes found him. He was pale and his eyes seemed to have sunk into their sockets. I knew he was battling. I also knew he was a fighter. I gave him a half-smile as if to tell him that I did not have the energy to speak. He drew a deep breath and then said, 'Bloody hell!'

It was good to see that the tents had already been pitched and all we had to do was to collect our belongings and unroll our sleeping-bags. The porters had arrived two hours or more before us, as though they had been on a gentle stroll. This had given them plenty of time to prepare the tents and the cooking fires.

I scanned the campsite trying to identify our tents and it occurred to me while doing so that we were sharing the site with another group of climbers. I could see two or three warmly clad people strolling around close to the tents.

As we drew closer, the inevitable banter from the porters indicated that they were in good spirits.

I then recognised the climbers. They were from Lucas Steyn's group. I immediately thought of David, his late arrival at Shira camp the previous night and his stoic departure with Brian that morning. It seemed like ages ago. I would never forget watching them go, not once looking back at us as they headed back toward the rainforest and the sunlit valleys below.

As I looked back down along our path, I could see Lava Rock surrounded by wisps of cloud. I could just make out the profile of the face. It looked more like Thomas's from that distance. So, that is how far David had come yesterday. I looked at Kibo Peak above and ahead of us. It was so close!

A wave of irritation swept over me. The last person I wanted to see right then was Lucas Steyn. I had no doubt that he would have some sarcastic things to say about us. He would be quick to tell us how clever they had been to have done their acclimatising at five thousand metres instead of at Shira, asking questions like, 'What time did you leave?' and so on … I doubted he would even mention David Joseph's name.

Jessie reached our tent first, taking with her our pillows, which she had unpacked. I carried the backpacks inside and unpacked the sleeping-bags. While Jessie spread the thin sponge mattress across the ground sheet, I unrolled the bags. There was no time to zip them together. The need for sleep was too urgent. Lowering myself onto my hands and knees, I flopped onto the softness of the down, too tired to remove my boots or my gortex jacket. I was probably well into the subconscious before my head had buried itself in the pillow, but a hard, cold sensation on my face put the brakes on any further descent into the underworld. I mustered the energy to open one eye to see what it was and I quickly recognised the lumps of ice that were now melting on the sleeping-bag. I realised that they were from the blizzard, carried in the collar fold of my jacket. It took a huge effort to prop myself up on my elbow and scrape the ice away, and that was the last I remembered before I heard a voice, which for a moment sounded again like that of my father. 'I have brought you some tea,' it said with a rough 'r' in the word 'brought'. I opened my eyes and sat up to see the silhouette of a man at the entrance to the tent. It was Thomas.

I remained silent, staring at him almost disbelievingly. Thomas must have wondered what was behind the perplexity of the eyes that held him and he backed off, apologising for waking me. Fully awake I said, 'No … no. Thomas … I'm sorry. Thanks for the tea. That will be very nice.'

'Thank you, Thomas,' I said again, adjusting my woollen beanie, which had reorganised itself while I slept. 'How're things going?'

'I'm very good,' he said in his even tone. 'But I think there is somebody who wants to see you. I told the man that he must wait until you have rested. Here are some biscuits to eat with your tea.'

I took the biscuits from him as a matter of courtesy. I couldn't eat a thing right then. They were oatmeal biscuits, which I usually enjoy, but there was no place for them in a stomach that seemed to have constricted itself. I sipped the sweet black tea and looked up to see Jessie with a frown on her face, massaging her forehead with her fingers.

★   ★   ★

Crawling out into the sunlight, I addressed Thomas, 'Where is this man?'

'He's in his tent. He is sick.'

Following behind Thomas, I zipped up my jacket and pulled my beanie over my ears.

Hugh was standing outside his tent, finishing his tea.

'Would you like me to come with you?' he asked.

'Sure, let's see what's going on.'

Thomas led us to a tent where three men were standing at the entrance. As I approached them, two of them looked away, scuffling their feet, their hands deep in the pockets of their windproof jackets, their shoulders pulled up against the cold. It looked almost as though they had been keeping a vigil outside the tent. From inside, I could hear someone coughing. One of the men said, 'We're sorry to trouble you, but we think he's quite bad.'

'Is it Lucas Steyn?' I asked. They did not answer.

The three men looked at each other briefly and the same man spoke again, 'He tried to get to the top early this morning. He was too ill and he turned back. He refused to let us take him all the way down to Shira. He's inside the tent. He knew you'd be here sometime today so you could see him. David told him that you were a doctor.'

Hugh came up behind me as I moved swiftly into the tent. There, propped up against his rucksack, was the man himself, Lucas Steyn. His skin was lemon-coloured, his lips were blue and his breathing was noticeably shallow and rapid.

'How is … David?' he asked, precipitating a spasm of painful coughs, which caused him to retch into a plastic container next to him.

If I had nurtured any thoughts of malice for that man until then, which I had, they quickly moved into the deeper nooks of my mind. Maybe it had something to do with the Hippocratic oath that I took with my fellow medical graduates when we qualified, part of which was an admonition that no suffering man or woman should ever be refused treatment. Maybe it was the fact that he still had it in him to ask after David. But there was something else … It was the realisation of what that mountain could do to a physically powerful and seemingly single-minded man. He was now at its mercy, too late to ask permission to know it and to be known. The mountain had said, 'No, not this time,' and I think he knew it. Seeing him from this close, I was convinced that I knew him from somewhere.

'Let me have a look at that sputum,' I said, reaching over to the yellow container he held up against his mouth. It was streaked with blood. My immediate thought was, 'We've got to get this guy out of here – quickly – otherwise he's going to die!'

One of those emergency medical images flashed through my mind: UPRIGHT MADAM. This is the mnemonic for the management of pulmonary oedema, a condition when the lungs begin to fill with fluid. It is usually a result of a failing heart, which cannot adequately clear the build-up of blood in the large pulmonary vein. This in turn causes a back-pressure overflow through the capillaries in the lining of the lung. Untreated, the patient literally drowns! In this case, the cause was staring everyone in the face – altitude sickness. Too high, too quick.

The mnemonic conjured up the image of getting the patient into an UPRIGHT position, which Lucas Steyn had already done instinctively. MADAM meant this – M for morphine, A for air (in the form of oxygen), D for diuretic, A for aminophyllin, a bronchial dilator, M for mineralo-corticoid or cortisone.

'Hugh! Please bring me the first-aid kit from my daypack,' I urged. 'Jessie will know where it is.'

I stood up and, grabbing Hugh by the arm, I whispered to him to tell the guide to arrange to get Steyn out of here and down the mountain … quickly.

Hugh left the tent and I asked Lucas Steyn to show me his tongue, which he did. It was a deep-purplish colour, indicating a serious lack of oxygen in his system. I felt for his pulse, amazed that the man had not already begun to slip in and out of consciousness. I measured it at almost two hundred beats a minute. We would have to act quickly.

Making no attempt to hide my intentions of getting him down the mountain I spoke sternly, in clear, short sentences.

'Listen to me, Steyn. David Joseph could have died on this mountain. It took a lot of courage for him to do what he did yesterday, turning back. Maybe if he'd been able to take a different pace, he might have been fine – he might even have made it to the top. He didn't, but at least he's okay. I wish I could say the same for you.'

'Now listen to me!' I said it again, bringing my face close to his. 'If we don't get you out of here soon, you won't be as lucky as David.'

Lucas Steyn dropped his eyes and then he made as if to speak. I stopped him.

'I don't want you to say a word. You're going to need all the energy you have to help us to sort you out.'

'Okay, doc ...' His voice was a hoarse whisper. I put a finger to my lips, indicating to him to be quiet. He began coughing again and this time he heaved desperately into the container. The large jugular veins on the side of his neck stood out angrily and I patted him on his back to assist in loosening the mucus that he could not cough up. My thoughts were racing. 'For Christ's sake, Hugh ... hurry up.' I was aware of my lips moving as I urged Hugh back to the tent. I felt for Lucas Steyn's pulse again, not so much to monitor it, but to maintain physical contact with him. It was all I could do right then.

Therapy is sometimes like that, Jessie had said. Sometimes there is nothing you can say to help a client. All you can do, is to *be there* with them.

'I don't want to die here ... okay?' said Lucas Steyn quietly. This was not a question. He was telling me. This time there was no coughing spasm.

'You aren't going to die here ... you're going to live. Now shut up!'

Lucas Steyn was pulling on his last reserves. A kind of wildness lit up his eyes. It wasn't there a couple of minutes ago. The last of his survival instincts had been activated. Will was the only thing that he had left.

Two minutes ago I had been convinced that he was on the way out, yet something had changed. Maybe it was the look in his eye that triggered the fight in me. He wasn't going to let go and neither was I. Sitting with him in those moments, I forgot about myself. I had shifted orbits. All the energy and meaning that I had derived from a scanning homeopathic world view of blizzards, dream profiles, bulimic volcanoes, vomiting obsidian, floods, the Garden of Eden and Olduvai Gorge began to shift. They seemed to come together, transforming into a world of intense allopathic focus. Naming the signs in front of me was more important than turning them into a metaphor. This was not the time for understanding the symbolic or deeper meanings of Lucas Steyn's fate, or mine. His destiny was in his hands and to a certain extent, his fate was in mine.

It was as if everything went into slow motion as I prepared myself for what had to be done.

'Where do I know you from, Lucas Steyn?' I whispered through clenched teeth. He did not hear me.

Hugh brought the first-aid kit with the emergency drugs in it.

'They'll be ready to leave in fifteen minutes,' he said, referring to the descent party.

'Thanks, Hugh. Please grip his biceps on his left arm. I want to get those veins up while I fill the syringes.'

I went for the cortisone first, knowing that it is a powerful anti-inflammatory agent, as well as a 'kick-start' drug for use in emergencies.

Lucas Steyn had a good ante-cubital vein in the crook of his left elbow and the needle went in easily. I slowly emptied the contents of the vial into his circulation and then disconnected the needle from the syringe, replacing it with the diuretic that I had drawn up in another syringe. I told Steyn that it may cause a burning sensation at the point of entry into the vein and I watched him wince ever so slightly as the diuretic entered his bloodstream.

Because there were no other signs of heart failure, I held back on the morphine. This was not only a powerful analgesic drug, it also caused peripheral pooling of blood if the central organs were congested.

Within a few minutes he was breathing easier.

'How're you doing?' I asked him.

'It feels a little easier now … It's just the headache.'

'Don't worry about that,' I assured him, 'the main thing is that you're breathing a little better. The headache will go when we get you out of here.'

He remained silent, taking in what I had said. I released the pressure of my thumb on the piece of cotton wool that I had placed on the puncture point on his arm, aware that Steyn was peering at me in a way that I could almost feel the heat of his focus.

'Where do I know you from?' he asked. I looked up at him and answered, 'I was going to ask you the same thing.'

'Didn't you live in Zambia?'

'Yes,' I said. 'Nkana, on the Copperbelt. I went to school there … primary school.'

'So did I,' he said. 'I was born there, but you left the primary school and went to boarding school in the Cape … you and the other English kids. I remember you now,' he said. 'You lived on a smallholding outside the town. All the big shots on the mine had places like that.'

He took a few breaths. 'Malcolm … Hamish Malcolm … that's right! I fuckin' hated you.' The tone in his voice caught me by surprise. His eyes communicated a combination of tease and malice.

If he was going to say anything I would have at least expected him to be a little more complimentary, I thought. There I was helping the man. I took what he said at face value and in a matter-of-fact way, I asked him, 'Why did you hate me?'

'Because you were *English*,' he said. 'All of you went to school in South Africa, and when you came back for the holidays, you guys were all full of shit, with all your right manners, all nice and sophisticated … like you owned the place. We used to call you guys "mommy's boys".'

My mind was immediately filled with memories of the town swimming-pool – the favourite place for punch-ups during the school holidays. I remembered that swimming-pool as a crucible of volatile adolescent hormones and, when old Pop Skinner, the weather-beaten pool superintendent, was out of sight, it turned into a territorial battleground.

'Do you want to know something, Lucas Steyn? I remember you too. You were about two or three years younger than me … a noisy little shit … always getting into fights. You hung around with a bunch of guys who were bigger than you. They were always fighting amongst themselves. You were the one who had the guts, you know.'

A faint smile broke through on Steyn's face.

'I remember a fight one day. You were there,' I continued. 'It promised to be a good one … one of those chronic Anglo-Boer wars between one of you and one of us. Blood and snot was already flying when I came across from where I had been lying in the sun. A big circle of spectators had rapidly formed around the two guys fighting. There was a lot of shouting going on … "Hit him! … Kick him!" There were some screams from the girls telling them to stop. The next thing, I was grabbed from behind. A pair of arms held my neck in a vice-like grip and I felt myself being pulled backwards. I remember twisting my body, unbalancing whoever it was that had attacked me. I spun round to see this little bloke getting up off the ground, clenching his fists to take me on again. It was you! Smaller than me as you were then, you came for me. I remember the expression on your face as you looked around to see if anyone was coming to help you. But no one came. I wanted to kill you. To this day I don't know what stopped me. You're lucky I was a mommy's boy. If I hadn't been, maybe I would have killed you. In any case, Pop Skinner arrived on the scene and you ran away.' Steyn avoided my eyes for a few moments. When they met again, I said, 'Now I've got you, Lucas Steyn.'

His eyes moistened. He smiled weakly.

'Pop Skinner …' said Steyn, remembering the old man. 'I remember that fight, you know. I didn't know it was *you*.'

'And you may enjoy hearing this,' I added. 'I also hated you … but not because you were Afrikaans, but because I envied you.

I envied your wildness … you didn't seem to be afraid of anything. Look at me,' I said, searching for his attention. I could see the tears were about to brim. He would not look at me.

'Look at me, Lucas Steyn!' I said again.

This time he raised his face to meet me, at the same time wiping his face with the back of his hand. He sniffed.

'What is it?' he murmured.

'I'm not afraid of you any more, Lucas. But I am afraid of what is much bigger than you and me − this mountain.'

I thought of telling him that if only he had been a little more afraid of it, things could have been different, but I left it. He didn't need any sermons.

'Can you help me?' he asked.

I wondered if he had ever asked anyone for help before.

'With that stuff that you have injected into me − will I be okay for the early-morning climb?'

Either the man was in complete denial or he was fighting this one to the bitter end. What was he trying to prove? I chose my words as carefully as I could.

'I'm afraid not, Lucas. First of all, I haven't got any more of that "stuff" to put into you. What's inside you is going to wear off in the next couple of hours. One dose is not enough to stop the fluid building up in your lungs. It will come back again unless you get to an altitude where there's enough oxygen for your body to heal properly.'

'But why haven't the others … or you … why aren't you also having altitude sickness?'

'We're all feeling it, Lucas. It affects people differently. Look what happened to David. One of our team also turned back this morning. You should've been with them. You can't believe that you, of all people, are vulnerable, can you? I think we're lucky that we got to you when we did. You could've been a goner, you know. Maybe there'll be another time … but at another pace … *pol-e, pol-e*. Now, let's get you out of here. There are still two hours or so of daylight and that will get you pretty close to Shira.

By then the cortisone will have worn off, but I want you to take this diuretic tablet by mouth and something for your headache.'

Hugh came back into the tent.

'They're ready to go,' he said. 'The other four in the group want to return home, as well. They're not feeling that grand either.' The guides had fixed up a hammock, in which they would carry Steyn.

'Maybe I should go as well,' I said to Hugh.

'No!' It was an emphatic response from Lucas Steyn. 'Thank you for looking after me … but I will be all right now. You must go on.'

'You must go on … *Engelsman*,' he repeated, calling me by the Afrikaans name for an Englishman. 'But I want you to take something with you for me, please. You must leave it at the top.'

He reached into the side pocket of his backpack and brought out a brown envelope.

'This belonged to my father. It had troubled him for a long time. He climbed this mountain a long time ago … as a bet … maybe forty years ago. He had to bring back proof that he had done it, which was difficult, because he did not have a camera. He brought back a bible that he'd found there at the top. Somebody from Nkana had left it there. On the inside page was the man's address. It was an Englishman whose name my father forgot. He said the man was very upset when my father showed him what he had brought. He told him that he should have left it there. My father felt bad. Later, he found these pages in his rucksack. He said he felt bad about it when he saw it, because he did not want to go and see the Englishman again. In any case, someone said that he had died. He didn't have the heart to throw all those pages away, so he kept them. When I told him I was coming here, my father, who is now getting on, asked me to bring these pages back to where, he said, they belonged.'

No words could describe what was happening to me when Steyn spoke, other than to say that my world once again went into slow motion. I heard with utmost clarity the echo of every vowel and every syllable that flowed from his mouth. I had heard it all before, somewhere.

I took the envelope from his hand, without taking my eyes off Lucas Steyn. I knew exactly what the contents were. Genesis had come home. Without a word, I nodded my head and put the envelope into the deep pocket on the inside of my windproof jacket. I said nothing more to Lucas Steyn. I just shook his hand and then I called for the hammock that would carry him down to Shira.

The late-afternoon sun was closing in on Mount Meru.

The guide came up to me and said they needed to get going.

As he was being carried out of the tent, Lucas Steyn turned to me and said, 'Doc … I don't hate all Englishmen. Thank you for the muti you gave me,' referring to the medicines.

'By the way, Lucas,' I said, 'I may speak English, but I am not an Englishman. I am as African as you are.'

★   ★   ★

Hugh, Jessie and I stood together in silence as we watched Lucas Steyn and his party walking away. The shadows of the late afternoon had already begun to stretch themselves into the valleys below. Soon it would be night.

Someone in their group coughed. It was a faint sound. It could have been Steyn. And then they were gone.

'Supper is ready,' said Thomas, breaking the silence. 'It's soup and bread.'

'Thank you, Thomas, but no thank you,' said Jessie. 'I just want to sleep.'

She had taken the words out of my mouth.

'No, miss Jessie, you must please eat … Come with me.'

So much had happened in the last hour that I had forgotten about sleep; I had forgotten about the mountain. I had forgotten about Jessie. I saw the wind blowing strands of her fair hair across her face. Usually she would gently sweep them away from her eyes but she was too tired, letting her hair tease her cheeks and her mouth.

'Come on, Jessie,' I said, 'I'll have a little soup with you. We're going to need it.'

Hugh seemed to have found his appetite. I watched him biting into a slice of bread with little clumps of cold peanut butter on it, chewing it vigorously and swallowing hard. Watching him eating was sufficient in itself. Whatever he swallowed seemed to be going down my own throat. Thomas, meanwhile, had poured the vegetable broth into our cups and the rising steam made it appear hotter than it actually was. By habit, I blew into the cup and took a sip of the lukewarm soup. I looked up to see Jessie cradling her cup in her hands. Hugh was seated next to her. He was holding a 'finger' of bread to her lips like a mother sometimes does when she is trying to get her child to eat … the way my mother coaxed me … the way I sometimes urged my own children to eat, pretending that the piece of bread was a little animal seeking shelter. Jessie nibbled at it reluctantly and then she held up her hand, signalling to Hugh that she had had enough.

From where I was sitting I could see the sun slowly merging into the black silhouette of Mount Meru. The dark clouds on either side of it were ringed in gold. It was a splendid sight in a splendid kind of silence. Behind me and to my right the full moon, in its ancient dance with the earth, emerged over the north-western shoulder of Kilimanjaro.

'When the moon is up here,' said Thomas, pointing into the sky to where the moon would be at its zenith, 'we'll be over there,' swinging his arm around and pointing to the edge of Arrow Glacier. 'The moon has been good to us,' he reflected.

'Tomorrow, it will show us the way.'

Just beyond the tents was a large cairn. It stood at the foot of the steep and final ascent of Kilimanjaro. A wave of deep respect for the mountain filled my belly. It was like the taste of venison.

★   ★   ★

For Jacob, there was still one more ridge to negotiate, one more orbit, one more mountain … Esau.

He had made his peace with Rachel's father, on his terms ...
*Let us make a covenant between us ... that this pillar of stones be a
witness that I will not pass over this heap to thee, and thou shalt not pass
over this heap and this pillar to me ...*

For Jacob, there was no going back. The cairn would stand as
a sign of respect, one man toward the other. It was a cairn that
not only indicated for Jacob his direction forward, but the direction from which he had come.

★ ★ ★

Scanning the mountain, I began to make out the ascent route,
tracing a line up the scree and into the gaps between the but-
tresses, the rock faces and the edge of the glacier. Above the glacier I saw what appeared to be a not too difficult scramble to the
top. For a moment I wondered ... was the mountain beckoning
me? Did it know that I had the book of Genesis with me and that
I was bringing it back? I tested all of my intuition to try to get the
mountain to speak to me, but there was no response. There was no
indication of any form of welcome. If anything, I was struck by a
great stillness in those rock faces ... a great indifference.

I looked at the mountain again and then at the cairn at the
lower edge of the glacier. It was the cairn that spoke to me. It was
pointing the way. A wave of apprehension filled my belly. There
was a taste of ice in my mouth.

Hugh had been watching me scanning the mountain. He said
there was a poet who once wrote about mountains. His name was
Ignatow.

'What did he say?' I asked. Hugh quoted him:

> *I should be content*
> *to look at a mountain*
> *for what it is*
> *and not as a comment on my life.*

'You've been reading my mail,' I said.

★ ★ ★

Jacob seemed to have little doubt as to where he was and where he was heading. He knew he was entering into the territory of his wild and neglected twin. He knew that he would have to confront him sooner or later. He sent out messengers to survey the territory ahead, telling them to convey to Esau that he had many things to offer, and that he wished ... *that he might find grace in his brother's sight.*

'The messengers represent everything that is *intuitive* in us,' said Jessie. 'Entering into the unknown, we sniff out whatever we can, for what lies in store. We are sometimes desperate for signs that things will work out. Sometimes there is little reassurance at all and sometimes we confuse wishful thinking with genuine intuition.'

The messengers returned to Jacob saying, *'We came to thy brother Esau, and also he cometh to meet thee ... and four hundred men with him.'* Then Jacob was greatly afraid ...

I could relate to that. I could not shake off the strange and uneasy feeling that I was on the edge of something significant. I was beyond the 'cairn' that marked the territory of where I had come from ... the world of the familiar. This was a different orbit. This was unprescribed. I was in Esau's territory and he was coming to meet me. It was scary.

Jessie told me this was a critical phase in the therapeutic relationship ... when the client was in the unfamiliar territory of his shadow, knowing that something was coming to meet him. It was the point when a client would often turn back, because of fear on the one hand, but on the other hand, because the client did not know *how* to confront his shadow. And so, he would fail to pitch up for the next session, or else he blamed you for his discomfort. 'Everything was okay until *you* came along,' clients would say. They sometimes saw Esau in the therapist.

'It is important to deal with this,' she said. 'If I cannot confront my clients, then I cannot expect them to confront themselves.'

I thought about my confrontation with Lucas Steyn. Had he been something of a shadow figure in me?

33

It was bitterly cold now. Even the porters were quiet. In fact, some of them were already asleep. For them the ascent was over. The next day they would pack up camp and head down to Mweka, which was where we would sleep. Mweka was on the edge of the rainforest. For some of us, who still had to ascend another thousand metres before heading down to where they would be, the next day was going to be one of the longest in our lives.

I could see a few porters huddled around a small fire which was fed very sparingly with the wood they had brought with them from the Shira plateau. There was no firewood at this altitude. Apart from the lichens which clung tenaciously to the granite rocks, the alpine desert could have been a reflection of the surface of the moon, inhospitable and indifferent.

Jessie and I cleaned our teeth together, sharing a mug of water to rinse our mouths. Like the wood for the fire, the water too had been brought up from Shira. It was precious.

Inside the tent and working by torchlight, we prepared for the night. We put on our full-length thermal underwear, polar-neck shirts, fleece-lined jackets and thermal socks, followed by thick woollen socks, climbing-boots and gloves. Finally, I pulled my beanie over my ears and then inched my way into my sleeping-bag. Jessie was struggling with the zip on hers.

I lifted myself onto my elbow and reached forward so that I could release a fold of material that had got caught up in the zip runner.

Every movement was slow, even something as insignificant as reaching out to help Jessie was exhausting. I had to take deep gulps of air to get my breathing back to a regular rhythm.

At last my head hit the pillow. I lay quite still, willing the strange world of sleep to take me with it. I was just about gone when a distant wail brought me back to the waking world. I opened my eyes and saw Jessie sitting up with her head between her knees. She had vomited her supper and she was crying.

'Are you okay?' I asked rhetorically. She stopped crying but she did not change her position. Then she spoke. 'Hamish ... I think it's all over for me. I can't go on.'

Pulling myself up onto my elbow again, I took a few breaths and then tried to answer her as deliberately as I could.

'No ... it's not,' I said. 'Not by a long way. What you're going through is to be expected. You'll be a lot better once you've had some sleep.'

Jessie had every reason to ask me how the hell I knew that. But she didn't. I was grateful for that. The fact of the matter was that I didn't know. I was digging deep into myself to find a reservoir of encouragement for her ... and for me.

Then I said to her, 'Jessie, if you're still like this tomorrow, if you feel that you've had enough, then I'll go down with you. And if you think that you're going to make it, then I think I can make it too. I am going to need you. I don't think I can do it without you.'

Jessie pulled my hand onto her cheek and letting out a long, deep sigh, she lowered herself onto her pillow. 'I wonder how the children are tonight?'

I knew she did not want me to answer her.

★   ★   ★

The guide map said this about day four – *You did not sleep as well as you might have expected. The headache got worse during the night, but goes soon after breakfast. Fruit, bread and jam were fine, but the sausage and egg were no-no. The blister that you should have attended to yesterday (but couldn't be bothered to) is now taped up and feels a lot better. Again, the first hour or so of walking is great, but then it is one step after the next. Around noon ... it starts to sleet and hail and the feeling of 'Why am I doing this' now gets asked aloud. Pulse is steady between 130–150 ...*

'Who is this guy?' I asked myself aloud.

34

IN SPITE OF all the clothing I was wearing, I struggled to keep warm. Any movement inside the sleeping-bag caused the cold air to be sucked in. I was miserable.

Lying still helped for a while but I couldn't stay like that for too long. My shoulders and hips, all those bony points, soon began to ache like they were screaming at me to change position. And when I did move, I had to try and get warm all over again.

I could hear voices coming from outside and then I heard laughter. It was the porters. I checked my watch. It was midnight. 'It's *today*,' I said to myself. 'It's about to happen, Jessie. Wake up!' I said, prodding the dark shape next to me.

'Hmmm,' she mumbled. 'I can't feel my fingers.'

'I know exactly what you mean,' I said, flexing and extending mine.

Thomas presented himself at the entrance to our tent. He had brought tea and biscuits 'Good morning, mister Hamish. You must eat this because you will not eat for a long time. We must leave in thirty minutes.'

I nibbled at the sweet biscuit and then tried to swallow what I had been chewing without tasting it. There was no way I could finish it, so I put what was left into the side pocket of my daypack.

We removed our fleece-lined jackets, putting on our down ones instead. All the other clothing from the night remained on our bodies. Over all of that we put on our gortex windbreakers.

We rolled up our sleeping-bags and put them with the other baggage for the porters to take to Mweka and then, with our head-lamps attached, we stepped out of our tent. The moon was waiting. There was something distant and matter-of-fact about it. I looked at it again. It was the coldest moon I had ever seen. It was heading west. I was heading east.

Hugh had a grin on his face when he greeted us. He was all set to go. I asked him what was up, and he shook his head. 'Nothing,' he said.

'That grin of yours is called frozen joy,' I commented.

Thomas gave us our instructions as to the order in which we were to walk. He would go first with Jessie behind him, followed by me, 'then mister Hugh, and then Julius. *Pol-e, pol-e,*' he cautioned for the umpteenth time.

★　　　★　　　★

Utterly alone and on the verge of one of those great dark nights of the soul, Jacob subjected himself to perhaps the most critical self-assessment session in biblical history. A war was going on in his psyche. He knew that it was his last chance to confront what had haunted him for so long.

What Jacob understood in the form of a haunting Esau, some of us understand better as that haunting voice, theory, dream, or the unfinished business that still has a grip on us and will not let go. It is a visceral hook.

'Jacob's great task on that night was ultimately one of god-making,' said Jessie. 'He would come to know the Esau in himself, as we sometimes have to. Esau is more than just a forgotten side of ourselves, by the way. In him is the wild energy that feeds us when we have to hang in. Jacob would discover what it was that supported him through those long nights when it seemed that there was nothing. On that night the artist in him would be free.'

★　　　★　　　★

We headed out past the tents toward the porters who had got up to prepare the tea and to say goodbye to us. They stood there smiling, greeting each one of us as we walked by. '*Habari.* I see you.'

197

I felt quite emotional. They were really *with* us, wishing us well. Maybe it was because I felt we were saying goodbye for a very long time. I began to miss them almost immediately. I greeted the cairn, touching it with a gloved hand. The outside temperature was way below freezing.

We were on the move, but our pace was unbelievably slow ... left foot ... right foot ... left again – three steps in twelve seconds, and it was going to get slower!

I thought of my father. I could see William Phiri urging himself up that slope. With that, a wave of energy injected itself into my body, circled my legs ... and then it was gone. I thought of him again and waited for the wave, but nothing happened. I was on my own. From then on, all help would have to come from something inside of me. Approval meant nothing.

Well into the ascent, my eyes were firmly set on Jessie's feet in front of me. I did not have the energy to hold my head up and look around me. I tried to take in the scenery but the full moon on the glacier and the sharp clinical outline of Kilimanjaro's crater edge above us failed to inspire. When I look back now, the view must have been spectacular, but right then it was easier to plod on watching Jessie's feet. When she moved, I moved. When she stopped, I muttered, 'Thank God.'

Jessie was hit by a wave of nausea. The biscuit that she had nibbled on earlier was on its way back. She did not have the time or the inclination to find a modest place to do what she had to. No one said a thing.

We kept on going slowly, slowly upward. With every stop I held onto my walking-stick with both hands at the top and rested my head on them, my feet slightly apart as I leaned forward to compensate for the slope. I knew that if I sat down, I probably would not have wanted to get up.

Eventually even the standing position could not stop me from falling asleep, for as soon as I closed my eyes, I was gone. I would be dreaming that the sun was out and I was walking on a stretch of white beach sand with waves gently lapping at my feet.

Someone was holding my hand. It was so beautiful there … so warm. I never wanted to leave.

'Hamish … mister HAMISH!' Suddenly it was dark. Was that snow over there?

'Mister Hamish … Come … We must go.' It was Thomas.

I do not remember how many times I went back to that stretch of sand and the sun, but Thomas kept bringing me back. It was wonderful to be there. I thought about telling the group to go on, that all I needed was a short nap and I would catch up with them, but I knew what would happen. It would be more than a short nap.

I thought about what was happening – the sun, the sea and someone holding my hand. I wondered if this was what dying was like … an overwhelming urge to let go … not wanting to come back again. And then I heard it from somewhere deep inside – '*You have not come here to die.*'

I kept talking to myself, telling myself to hang in. I reminded myself of my father's ashes … that they were going to one place only … to the top. I was coming to bury my father. I thought about Lucas Steyn and wondered about the hold his father still had on him. As he was trying to outdo his father, had his father in some way buried him?

We came to a steep section of scree, a sloping head of loose rocks and gravel. For every two steps up, we slid back one. It was hell. Sensing that the mountain was not going to let us off the hook, I began to feel angry. I then began wrestling with the characters of Genesis. I would not let *them* off the hook. They were coming with me, every goddamn one of them.

35

AND JACOB WAS left alone; and there wrestled a man with him until the breaking of the day.

… Jacob lifted up his eyes, and looked, and, behold, Esau came … And Esau ran to meet him, and fell on his neck and kissed him; and they wept. For a moment I thought about Lucas Steyn.

★ ★ ★

A swishing sound above me made me look up. Two alpine swifts flew by and I watched them in their curving flight down and across the glacier. The swifts and the dawn had come to meet me. The early-morning light was like a medicine and I felt a surge of optimism. I did not know how long it was going to last, but the tiredness seemed to have left me as well. Thomas was looking down at me with the hint of a smile on his face. He knew what was awaiting us. Immediately above him was a cairn.

Hugh had been resting behind me. He had watched me falling asleep on my walking-stick. He had also seen the alpine swifts. Perhaps he too had experienced the surge of optimism that I had just felt. He did not ask me how I was. Instead, he gently prodded his stick into my daypack to make physical contact with me. Then he quoted the early salute to the mountain. I joined him in the last two lines, echoing at the top of my voice …

'… but bend me beyond my endurance …
And let me break …'

★ ★ ★

We were cold and we were tired but it did not matter. We kept moving. We crossed the great volcanic ridge of Kilimanjaro and headed toward the final snow-covered slope of Kibo Peak. It did not matter that we went slowly. It did not matter that I was dragging my feet through the snow. Every step counted. Every twist in the path meant one thing. I was getting there. I refused to break.

'How far now, Thomas?' I asked him. I was dead serious.

He looked at me somewhat in disbelief and then smiled at Hugh and Jessie who were standing with him. How did they get there ... I wondered?

'Come and see,' he said. 'The sun is rising.'

There was nowhere else to go but down.

The next thing we were hugging each other – Jessie, Hugh, Julius and Thomas. I hugged Jessie again and as we held each other, we both wept quietly. We had made it!

★   ★   ★

Reading a fraction under six thousand metres, the sign tells you that you are on the very roof of Africa. Next to it is a wooden box, an open container for messages and other odds and ends that climbers have left behind, like flags, caps and walking-sticks.

I slowly walked up to the cairn that marks the highest point on the mountain and taking off my right glove, I wet my palm with my tongue. I then put my hand on the solemn pile of stones and stood back.

'So, this is where we are ...' I whispered.

Jessie came and stood with me while I removed from my daypack the small branch of the *Ziziphus*, holding it up to examine its two rows of thorns. With the tip of my right index finger I tested the forward-pointing thorn. It was sharp enough to leave a small dimple in the skin. Then with the same finger, I tested the thorn that hooks backward. It too was sharp and in the dimple I saw a tiny bead of fresh blood. I licked it and swallowed. I then removed from my jacket pocket the envelope that Lucas Steyn had given me, asking Jessie to hold it. 'What's this?' she asked.

'I'll tell you on our way down,' I replied.

I unpacked the old bible that belonged to my father and put the cover to my nose to smell it. It had a sweet, leathery smell. I then opened the brown envelope and in it were the missing pages from Genesis. Many of them lay loose and, as I removed them, I thought once more of the ongoing pattern of creation. As gently as I could, as if taking care of each character that I had come to know along the way, I placed the pages in the bible and closed the tin. I put it into the wooden box next to the sign and then looked toward the north ... somewhere in the direction of Scotland.

The clouds were beginning to close in and, looking around me, I saw Thomas was watching me.

I took out the box that carried my father's ashes. In silence, I remembered my mother and my father and then I removed a stone from the cairn. Into the gap where the stone had been, I poured the volcanic-like remains. Into the same gap, I placed the branch of the *Ziziphus mucronata*.

A cold shiver wracked my body. I felt no anger at that altitude. It was okay. I could go now. The ancestors had come home.